Journey to no

First, how to focus
when drowned in fog,
a haar that tempted
my eyes to close
safe in sleep.
Sofa beckoned.
This journey was
sickness, grief, loss.
Unrelenting.

Yet the gestation of this book
and birth compelled.
This was mine,
held close.
The words,
questions
the feelings -
all mine.
Mine to share
editors then
with you.
Feedback triggers fear.
Doubt.

Again my cancer
trying so hard to win.
Can I keep going?
And yet
I can offer you this.
It's for you
and……me.
I captured this
to be heard.
To know the struggle
is for more than
a knitted baby cardigan
a blog of part-truths.
A book I wanted to read.
To write
and live on
when my journey is complete.

Content of Book

Part One

Prologue

My story

Introduction to the Ten Elements

Part Two

10 Elements to living well with cancer and long-term conditions

Part Three

Reflections from my journey

All rights reserved. No portion of this book may be reproduced, copied, distributed or adapted in any way, with the exception of certain activities permitted by applicable copyright laws, such as brief quotations in the context of a review or academic work. For permission to publish, distribute or otherwise reproduce this work, please contact the author at **audrey.l.birt@gmail.com**.

Author
Audrey Birt
M.P.H, B.S.c, RGN, Dip HV
Diploma in Gestalt inOrgisations. Certificate in Coaching and Coach Supervision
Edinburgh, Scotland
September 2023

Part One

Prologue

The stimulation to finally write Finding Better Times was the coronavirus pandemic lockdown announcement. I had developed this book idea for some time but never managed to commit to it and formulate the concept I was holding in my head.

It was a month into lockdown, and I was recovering from a virus, when I was finally ready to write. This was a unique time, creating uncertainty and an existential anxiety like I have never known. The loss experienced by so many was overwhelming, even as a bystander. At the same time the survival instincts and the courage shown were inspiring.

Each morning I was glued to the new statistics, the new findings from fresh and vital research my latest addiction. It was like reading a sci-fi detective novel and the baddy was a virus that was beyond our reach and our understanding.

But for me, along with many others, the space created by being in lockdown offered a freedom to think and reflect. It was a potentially creative void that stimulated a bubbling desire for change.

Those of us with serious illness like cancer and long-term conditions carried a particular fear. A very worrying narrative emerged. As rising death rates were announced, the caveat was given that they had any been in the elderly or those with long-term conditions. The 'not us' was the silent acknowledgement. As if our deaths were acceptable.

There was a strong push back against this attitude, but the issue remains. Decisions were made assuming what is best for people, or prioritising safety from infection before the human need for connection. Notably there was and is a lack of asking the most vulnerable what would help at this stage. Assumptions rarely make good policy.

My experience as a nurse, a health charity director, and very importantly as a person living with the impact of breast cancer, and with disability due to rheumatoid arthritis and a benign spinal growth, puts me in a unique position to develop these Ten Elements. The elements are to enable greater wellbeing after serious illness like cancer and for those living with long-term conditions. The Elements aim to support us to self-care and self-manage our conditions and allow to achieve greater wellbeing.

It's taken me some time to get to this stage of the book as I've had yet another diagnosis of breast cancer which has now spread to my liver. As well as being shocked with the confirming of a stage 4 cancer I have been motivated to complete this work and share it with anyone who can be helped by this Journey to Better Times.

My deepest wish is that this book helps you find hope and purpose in challenging times.

My story

I grew up in a village in Fife. Not the kind where people go for their holidays, I admit. It was shaped by the local employers mainly: the mines and the railway. The folk who worked in the railway considered themselves a step up from the miners and their families. My father had found himself working in the mines locally to be able to keep his family and gradually worked his way up to be an official. So, I was in the mining group with no understanding of anyone being better or worse than me. It was a happy childhood. In the summer we had great freedom and warnings like 'if you come back drowned, I'll kill you' went unheeded as we played on homemade swings over the river! In the autumn we went for walks and picked rosehips which we took to the pharmacy, where it was made into rosehip syrup, rich in vitamin C. We got malt extract and cod liver oil to boost our vitamins B and D; the malt extract was much nicer. We ate homemade soup. We grew vegetables and ate meat from the local farm. The fishman delivered fish on a Wednesday fresh from the harbour at Pittenweem, a fishing village on the East Neuk of Fife. Our lives were healthy, with a diet that's hard to emulate now with global food industries influencing our intake of food, especially sugar.

The primary school was a short walk around the corner, so I went home for lunch. Our days were mapped out, with Sunday School on Sunday where my friendship group widened. It was a happy and healthy environment: I was fortunate. But I was a sickly child. Every winter I coughed, and I had huge, infected tonsils. In adulthood I was diagnosed with asthma which made such a difference with treatment, but in those times a tonsillectomy was thought to be the solution. It was in hospital for this procedure that my fascination with hospitals, public health and healthcare, and nursing, began.

At school I was encouraged to go to university, and I told I was too clever to be a nurse. That bemused me at the time but now infuriates me of course. My other passion was English. My whole life I've loved books. One of my weekly treats was a visit to the library. It was alongside the local doctor's surgery, and it was sometimes hard not to notice the conversations going on in there. But I was not at all interested: it was Enid Blyton, and *Anne of Green Gables* that I cared about. I wondered about being a librarian, but my Mum felt compelled to point out that I couldn't read books and drink coffee all day. It was my sister who found the compromise, and I studied nursing at the University of Edinburgh, the first degree of its kind.

I hadn't enjoyed secondary school, but I loved this degree. It was a course that recognised that nursing was a complex mix of science, human biology, psychology, communication skills and knowledge of health as opposed to illness. Of course, we also had to gain the practical skills and knowledge. In the final year we did a dissertation, and I chose to study breast cancer. My Dad's Aunty Chrissie had recently had a mastectomy as had our next-door neighbour. Her daughter and I had been friends since preschool and so I saw its impact. I wanted to study this illness that was affecting so many people close to us. On the course I'd also studied anatomy and physiology, major systems and diseases like heart disease and cancer; and we also had a strong focus on person-centredness, compassion, mental as well as physical health, and palliative care. The trajectory of breast cancer care meant it was appropriate to bring in all these elements. Studying it and interviewing people, I learned so much and was deeply affected by the impact on people and their families. I look back on this and wonder if I had a premonition of some kind, or if it was just an irony that it would shape my own life too.

Around this time, I met my husband, Andrew, and we went on to have two children - and a few cats and dogs too. We were living near Loch Lomond and most weekends involved a dog walk somewhere stunning. With rainwear on of course. For a while his work took him travelling all over the world, therefore my work needed to be local, to combine with childcare. My career took me into community work, and I trained as a health visitor. The public health role was a real interest and I loved working with children.

When we first moved to the West of Scotland I went to work as a practice nurse as there no suitable jobs in health visiting. I loved being a practice nurse in a small community. The focus of my role was preventive, supporting people with long-term conditions and people with depression. I did teach breast awareness so when a friend found a lump, I encouraged her to have it checked out. She was in her 30's too so we -her friends-weren't too worried. But we were wrong, it was cancer. Her family and friends were so shocked. She needed a lumpectomy, chemotherapy, and radiotherapy. A group of us organised taking her to the hospital for radiotherapy. I was allocated the last evening on the basis I was the nurse and would know what to do. Truthfully, I was nervous as I wasn't in work mode. This was a dear friend, and my emotions were raw. And as expected, that last treatment was harrowing psychologically. We hugged while she sobbed out the tension, the enforced smile for months, the fear, the 'what now'? I have a very vivid recollection of that evening.

Like many of her friends I had become rather overanxious about my breasts. They were very hormonally affected, and an examination found lots of lumps that varied with my cycle. That said I did notice a pain in my left breast in the upper outer quadrant. I told no one and monitored it. I told myself off for my imaginary illness. As time went on, my friend's life was moving on and we were all less absorbed by it all. But the strange thing is the pain did not go. It was a niggle like toothache, and it started to waken me at night. I was still trying to ignore it. It was a rare symptom. One evening as my daughter came down for a snuggle on the sofa, after her bath. She cuddled in and put her head right on the spot. I yelped like the dog when I stood on her toes. I finally got it checked. The GP thankfully took it seriously and shortly afterwards I was at the breast clinic.

Breast clinics have their own vibe. The air is thick with fear. That word *cancer* has an impact like no other. The tangible anxiety often comes even more from the partners and friends accompanying the women (and men too of course). Books are no good when it's hard to concentrate, and these were the days before mobile phones were able to distract. A good excuse to have your head down and at all costs avoid eye contact. That first time I found myself watching the women with the tell-tale headscarf. How would I cope if it were me? But I knew only 1 in 10 lumps presented to the clinic resulted in a positive diagnosis of cancer. The odds were good.

You know already I was that one that probably had cancer, but at first it wasn't clear and the area small (the pain had identified it at an early stage). They decided it could be managed by watch and wait meantime. I left speedily, like a cork out a bottle, just in case they changed their minds. I got on with my life. Six months later there was little change, so it was moved to a year. I became blasé. I even started a part time master's in public health. I was balancing this with working part time and bringing up my two primary school aged children and not forgetting the cat and dog. I collapsed in the evening, but I was happy, and fit after taking up running 10ks.

The year review came along. I took a book to read for an essay and planned to visit the library after my appointment. Andrew offered to come. Do not worry, it will be fine said I, with a shrug.

It wasn't. It had grown and the mammogram showed a small area that looked like it might be an invasive tumour. It was small but needed to be assessed. I had a biopsy, it was cancer. Two lots of surgery followed and radiotherapy, no chemotherapy as it had not spread, thankfully. I was told, don't worry, you will live.

Finally, I could breathe more easily again. Until within a few weeks it became clear that my Dad was becoming increasingly unwell. He had been diagnosed with prostate cancer the previous year and it had rapidly progressed. As my five weeks of radiotherapy finished, my father moved into a hospice. Two weeks after my radiotherapy finished my dad died.

I was close to him. His hug could cure anything for me. He also brought me up to be political and particularly to want to make a better life, not just for some but for all. By the time of the miners' strike in the 80s he was an official in a management role and had just retired. Every evening we would chew over the latest events. We cried together when the beaten miners returned to their pits, their broken communities fragile - and finally finished when shortly afterwards all the pits were closed as predicted. My Dad always said no one should have to earn their money hewing coal from the ground but the cruelty of these final years shaped my politics. I still (26 years later) want to call him when some political drama occurs. Goodness knows what he would make of these times. I feel relieved in a way that he didn't live to see the destruction of the democracy that he risked his life for.

But I lost him, my dad, my hero, just at the time I needed him most. For a time, I didn't know how to keep going, but I did, just putting one foot in front of the other. And shedding a lot of tears. I was grieving for so much. A wise older GP said to me one day when my face told the story, 'There will be better times', and he was right. Hence the title of this book.

Six months after my treatment had finished, we planned a trip to Paris without the children: a week off work to revisit our favourite place. I realised during the visit my energy was severely depleted. The more I tried to push through, the less I could do. *Can we stop for a coffee?* was my call all week. I returned to work, and I felt scared; I didn't know where I would find the energy to keep going.

One day I was driving to Loch Lomond over the hill from home, and for a moment I considered driving off the road. I felt a strong pull, but I feel sure I didn't want to die. I wanted to stop feeling what I was feeling. I need this to stop. Thankfully, I realised then, I had to stop saying I was fine, and to ask for help. My GP signed me off work and I found a counsellor to talk to. The release of the counselling was so helpful, and the rest made a tremendous difference.

I was so relieved to get back to work. I saw my goal as getting back to who I was before the cancer and losing my dad. It was years later I realised that I had changed; physically, mentally, and emotionally. I was different and no amount of denial of impact stopped that being true. I knew intellectually that denial got in the way of adapting and accepting, but I was still working hard, in the only way I knew how, trying to hold on to a life that no longer existed. And yet, I would continue to push through. In those days if someone asked if I was tired, I couldn't answer. I didn't know what a life without tiredness looked like.

As time went on and the children got older, my career really shifted. I became a nurse manager and then worked on health care redesign. Improving care had been my passion since my own and my father's lived experience of it. I became the National Director of what is now called Diabetes Scotland. I learned so much working in a different sector and it was there I really saw the gap between what mattered most to people and what services offered. I'd thought I knew this as a nurse, but I realised that we were designed in the medical model and not what mattered most to people.

I worked long hours and travelled all over the UK but mostly to London. This was the time when devolution of healthcare was really affecting change. It was my role to lead the challenge of convincing people in London of when and how Scotland differed from the rest of the UK. It was a difficult stage for many of us. I connected with fellow leads of UK charities in Scotland. We were often very alone in the roles, and they became a great source of support. A few of us decided to work together to secure funding for what was originally the Long-Term Conditions Alliance Scotland and has since become the Health and Social Care Alliance Scotland. Its vision is for disabled people and those living with long-term conditions to have a strong voice to influence services and policy as well as enjoy their right to live well and free of discrimination.

Our first area of focus was to develop the self-management strategy. At that time, it could have been very medically focussed; however, we ensured it was shaped by people with long-term conditions and the disabled. This was unique and influenced the future of long-term healthcare in many ways. I was chairing it (and leading it alongside the development manager initially) as well as leading Diabetes Scotland. It was busy but we all felt we were making a difference.

One evening I came home, and Andrew drew my attention to an advert: Breakthrough Breast Cancer (merged with others to become Breast Cancer Now) was setting up an office in Scotland. They were looking for an Executive Director for Scotland. I knew right then I wanted to be the person to develop the role. Once I met the team in London, I thought I would enjoy the culture and setting up a new team in Scotland to deliver improvement for people affected by breast cancer.

So, dear readers, I got the role, based in Edinburgh. It was exciting, scary, and lonely until I got a small team together. The team were a great mix of people in skills and experience but all of us with a great energy to make a real difference to people affected by breast cancer in Scotland. I even worked with a Professor I had first met as a student nurse when we were at the beginning of our careers.

Three years into the role, we moved, after 20 years in the West of Scotland; we were sad and excited. The move did take its toll on us. I was also referred to the local breast clinic, following up an issue I had on my right breast, the one that had been previously healthy. This was around 15 years after my first diagnosis, so I wasn't concerned, but didn't want to ignore it. I was right at one level, as my right breast was fine. But around the scar on my left breast there was an area of cancer; non-invasive but needed removed. I was initially prepared for a mastectomy, but the multidisciplinary team said I needed only a small operation and no radiation as I had had it there before. I had another wide local excision and later some reconstructive surgery which had a bigger impact than I realised.

The return of cancer too shocked me, and honestly more than I would have expected. I hadn't realised I was still at risk of recurrence. Nonetheless I knew it was an early diagnosis and I thought I'd hardly need time off. Little did I know how wrong that was. I struggled when I returned to work. I cried easily, and I was exhausted, especially when travelling. That's when I started to write a blog, to hold the boundary between my work and my life, which were at huge risk of merging. I focussed the blog mostly on work, and I rediscovered a love of writing. But I didn't share everything. For example, when I was off recovering, I was told by the charity that I was running out of paid sick leave, as I had also been ill with asthma while trying to recover from the first lot of surgery. I was shocked. I had rarely in my life taken sick leave. And as Director, until a cover was put in place for me during the last surgery, I had still stayed in touch and answered emails.

I realised I was one of the statistics, one of those whose breast cancer had affected their career. I lost trust that my organisation would support me and realised that if I were sick again, I would be only on statutory sick pay. I decided to leave rather than drop my hours, as part-time working was full of risk in a role like this. The travel up and down to London was just exhausting and frankly my life at that stage was a struggle. So, four and a half years after setting up the post, I left without a job. After I left, I realised I was depressed, a common aftermath of breast cancer. I still wonder if I would have made a different decision had I been well.

My experience was wide and deep, I had been a finalist for Female Director of the Year for the Institute of Directors. I like setting things up, I realised, and the coaching development work I had done, alongside a diploma in Gestalt in Organisations, made me well placed to set up my own organisation, Birt Associates, as an executive coach and consultant. Again, I had started from scratch, but I quickly found people sought me out. Of course, not everything worked out, and I had some painful lessons to learn, but I really loved what I was doing. I enjoyed not only the coaching and organisational change work, but also developing expertise at enabling the voice of people with experience of cancer or long-term conditions to shape policy.

I was approaching my 60th birthday and thriving in my new role, I could care for myself, and I had been invited to work in some interesting areas. I was also planning to celebrate my birthday all year. I attended for a routine follow up in the December before my birthday in February. I had noticed some thickening around my scar. It was scanned. Two mammograms and a needle biopsy later and yes, you guessed, the cancer was back.

This time I was angry. Really?! I had been feeling stronger at last, and now this. My choice was for a mastectomy and for a *latissimus dorsus* flap reconstruction. It absolutely knocked me off my feet. I was breathless for months and it was only after steroids for an asthma flare-up that I improved. And it was only then I realised how much I was struggling with my mobility. People commented on my limp. So, I pursued everything to help me get back to normal. I went to (lots of) physios, an osteopath, a sacro-cranial massage therapist, and I had also tried everything from Pilates to Feldenkrais. I am afraid to total the financial cost of it all.

Having tried everything, I went back to the GP in June 2017 who sent me for an MRI. The GP phoned with the result when I was on holiday in August in a remote village in Bulgaria. She said I had growth on my spine (most likely benign) pressing on the spinal cord at T11-12. She said go to A&E now for a CT scan. That was a great end to the holiday! I knew then that our love affair with the wee house in Bulgaria we bought 12 years earlier was over. I was told it was a rare development; spinal surgery was possible but carried a 50% risk of paralysis. But, doing nothing carried a high risk of that anyway. A rock and a hard place. I got a second opinion, I waited to see if it would progress - it did. I was starting to need a wheelchair to get out and about. I got a mobility scooter, which I loved and finally the following June 2018 I had the surgery. Andrew and my daughter Cat walked with me to the operating theatre. Their distress as they left me has stayed with me; all my fear and loss, reflected in their faces. The surgeon, who was kindness itself, said he would phone them once I was out of theatre. This was 9am. He called them at 11pm.

The surgery was complicated; the growth was stuck to my spinal cord. Each time they tried to remove it, I bled. I almost died. They couldn't remove the growth but tried a work around. I was 5 days in ICU (Intensive Care Unit). Then over a week in HDU (High Dependency Unit). From there I got to the ward, and I was gradually able to walk, slowly and carefully, with an aid and after pain relief. I was told how well I was doing until I slid in the shower and developed a spiral fracture of my left tibia. My right leg was where I got all the pain. Despair affected me for a while but with grim determination, around 10 days later, I got home.

I could walk a few steps with a walking aid and fortunately I never lost bladder or bowel function, which was another risk. Was the operation a success? I do not know but I'm still much as I was after surgery. Less pain and distress, but not very mobile. I was a wheelchair user from then on, but frankly the wheelchair was so welcome to help me move around and relieve pain. Alongside my mobility scooter, it was my new best friend.

In September 2018 I went to my follow up appointment to the breast clinic. The Prof looked at me in the wheelchair and his eyes welled with tears. We were both crying. He examined me and was quite happy. 'I could not cope if you found anything', I said. We agreed to delay a mammogram until next year. But the following month I saw my GP about a lump around my thoracotomy scar and reconstruction scar. The Prof and GP arranged for a CT (computerised tomography) scan of my abdominal area and my chest too.

I had a follow-up with the neurosurgeon, and he was happy with me, but I picked up something in his demeanour. Andrew noticed it too. Was he not happy with me? I felt guilty, without reason. It troubled me. The breast clinic also wanted to see me of course. Off we went to a new patient clinic. Which seemed strange: *I am hardly new*, I thought. It was December by then and I was stronger, but not so strong that I was not devastated by the news - I had breast cancer again. It had shown up on the CT scan. It was an aggressive tumour so that scan probably saved my life.

Yet again we were knocked over by the news. Instead of chemotherapy I was put on exemestane, orally, to shrink the tumour. The follow-ups showed it was working. Surgery was planned for May. In the meantime, I saw a genetic counsellor and decided to be tested for BRCA 1&2. My family history meant it was unlikely. My Dad had prostate cancer and his aunt had breast cancer. I was not worried about the result as that's not many people affected in our family. (I never learn, do I?)

I got a phone call and learned I have the BRCA2 mutation. This means that anyone carrying that gene has a 45-85% lifetime risk of breast cancer- oh well, that explained a lot. And a 10-30% lifetime risk of ovarian cancer. So, I had a mastectomy with no reconstruction. I could not put myself through reconstruction then. I took a while to recover and heal as my immune system was struggling.

I was due to have my remaining ovary removed in December 2019, but I had a monster of a chest infection that took several weeks and antibiotics to heal. It was reorganised for February 2020, just after my 64th birthday. It went smoothly and I was home that night. In early March we had a week away in Argyll with my sister and her husband and our dogs. I even got in the hot tub as it had a hoist. Life was looking up-ish.

The soundtrack to that break was coronavirus. We avidly read each report. At that stage Italy had mass graves. We were really alarmed and expected things to be closed soon. That weekend we returned home to lockdown. Yet again, I had thought this year I would be better and have some fun. 2020 had other plans for all of us. Coronavirus or COVID-19 showed us the impact of an unknown virus, on short and long-term health.

I realised then there would never be a better time to share what I have learned about living well with serious illness like cancer and long-term conditions.

Introduction to the ten elements

It's my intention through this book to use all of the experience which has given me such a deep and personal knowledge of the experience of serious illness, including breast cancer diagnosed four times and nearly dying in surgery. Having all of that to recover from has been a massive, life shaping challenge. In adjusting to disability, I've learned that process is never linear, and comes with enormous adjustments and losses. I've learned as well, that being a wheelchair user is not the hardest thing to adjust to, for me at least. Its living with chronic pain that's so hard and life-depleting.

This time has provided rich learning and enabled my professional and academic knowledge to be combined with expertise gained from life. The Journey to Better Times is a unique blend of them, with some wisdom gained along the way.

The Ten Elements I have developed are guided by all of this. I describe them within the context of my own learning, often from mistakes. I've learned that those living with the trauma that long-term illness causes need support for internal shift and change, as well as monitoring of traditional biological markers like blood sugars or blood pressure. So my insights take the reader through deepening of self-knowledge and understanding of what matters, in order to find our strengths and intrinsic drivers that will guide therapeutic choices. I know now, that without self-care and self-compassion we will not give ourselves the best chance of recovery. These insights sit alongside traditional medical approaches and therefore each chapter also contains some key reflections for professionals.

In many respects this book is part of my own processing and recovery but mostly I've used my precious strength to write this in the hope others going through their own illness and trauma will gain fresh insights and skills that improve their own experience and life transition. The aim is for us to strengthen our innate capacity.

My knowledge and deeper understanding have also been shaped by participating in Dr David Reilly's The WEL (wellness enhancement learning). His lifelong studies and research have significantly informed my work and my life.

As the pandemic advanced, we saw desperate scenes of people critically ill and dying from this virus. But that is not all: we are now also seeing a wide range of people developing long covid. COVID-19 is a devastating virus that is airborne and is spread by people who are asymptomatic and although for some the impact is short-lived, it can leave survivors with long-term, often devastating effects. This is a dangerous and powerful foe.

We know health and social care professionals are disproportionally affected by the virus themselves - particularly if they are from BIPOC (black and indigenous people of colour) groups. This virus reminds us that we are not either patients/clients or professionals: this affects all of us, all humanity. Working alongside each other with mutual respect will provide shared healing.

The arrival of COVID-19 was the final push to write this book and help people with their journey, whatever their health issue. It's also to provide hope that you can find a place of wellbeing, whatever your condition and stage of illness. Every major transition changes us, even if it is a happy one. I don't mean in the 'cancer was a gift' sense, but to acknowledge the impact of personal transformation. The book aims to help you work with those significant adjustments.

I recommend keeping a journal as you read and capture your reflections as they too transform.

Introducing the ten elements

The next section briefly describes all ten elements, or 'Insights', to support wellbeing. The more detailed sections can be read in any order you want, but what follows allows an incremental shift in understanding. Each 'Element' is followed with reflections for professionals.

Element One:

Know who you are

When we are diagnosed with a significant illness, we are normally given a list of Dos and Don'ts. The premise this works on is that we're all much the same, and all we need to do is what they tell us, and all will be well. What is important is to take time to be with yourself. Even friends and family can join in the 'you need to do…' brigade. But the point of this section is to help us deepen our understanding of ourselves. Going through illness and diagnosis with long-term conditions makes us shift on our axis. This can be hard to recognise, so this chapter gives time to reflect, to make choices and to answer questions that enable deeper understanding of our needs. There are several exercises to work through, which will help gain insights for wellbeing and for life.

Element Two:

Understand your values

This chapter helps to understand the values that shape you and come to know more about what matters to you. Often values we live by are subconscious: they have been shaped by family, teachers, loved ones, or professionals, and we live them without exploring them. Here are exercises to help get to know the key values that shape our lives and gives life meaning. The more future decisions are aligned to our values, the more fulfilled our lives will be. The chapter will help you explore values and ensure insight to inform significant decisions in your care, support and in life.

Element Three:

What are your strengths?

Instead of focusing on what is wrong with you, this chapter will ask what you *can* do and build on that. In times of stress, we can lose sight of our strengths, believing perhaps they have gone, and this adds to our distress. What can be helpful is to bring into awareness those parts of ourselves that are resilient and build on this core. The chapter will also help notice if 'shoulds' are common in your daily language and how to notice and change that. 'Shoulds' can undermine our confidence in our innate coping mechanisms.

Element Four:

Find out who and what lifts you up and brings you joy

It may not be who or what you think it is. Once you understand, the message here is to see more and do more of that. You will also start to notice who or what brings you down and develop the learning to let go of that or them. This chapter helps you gain insight into your own reactions and how you typically relate when faced with serious illness and/or trauma. It suggests ways you can manage the storm. In addition, it helps you identify where the best support will be and encourage you to accept that.

Element Five:

Working with your health and social care team as a partner in care

Having worked through the other chapters you are in a good position to understand what's best for you and how this guides what treatment decisions to make. The chapter will help you understand what a 'partner in care' is and how you can play a full part in your medical and therapeutic decisions.

Element Six:

Learning and support from people with lived experience

How to understand your condition through trusted non-medical sources and connect with others who share the experience of living with the same or similar conditions. This can be through people you know and trust and / or with groups or charity peer programmes. Charities often offer opportunities to meet with others living with your condition. This chapter will also help you navigate the complexity of information and advice on the kind of sources to trust and explore.

Element Seven:

Learn how to process what has happened

This involves considering diagnosis, treatment and living with the new situation. To really move forward it's important to process what has happened - physically, emotionally, and neurologically. A spell in intensive care will often result in a form of PTSD, for example, and denial of impact will not help in the long-term. This chapter is about processing and understanding PTSD and body/mind engagement.

Element Eight:

Understanding grief and loss

Understand more about grief and loss and approaching end of life. Grief and loss may be relevant at any stage in a disease and change in condition. This chapter will help you navigate loss and grief, explore the myth of closure, and understand some cultural norms and taboos. It will also support those facing death and how to plan it with others to achieve the outcomes you want.

Element Nine:

Nature, nurture and food matters

The chapter explores the importance of healthy eating, exercise, and human connection to support a healthy immune system, especially whilst recovering from or living with serious illness and long-term conditions. Why Vitamin D3 and Omega 3 matters in prevention and recovery from illness; the influence of diet on both physical and mental health.

Element Ten:

Compassion is core

The focus is on self-compassion and compassion for others as core parts of wellbeing. Part of this is self-care, accepting support and being able to ask for help with things like mental wellbeing. The chapter also explores kindness and selfcare.

These are the ten insights for holistic health and wellbeing. They are of value individually, but most effective when combined. I recommend that you keep a notebook or journal, to capture your thoughts and learn from the various exercises. The journal may also help you to see how things are changing for you.

Part Two

The Ten Elements

Element One:

Know who you are

When we are diagnosed with a significant illness, we are often given a list of Dos and Don'ts. The premise this works on is that we're all much the same, and all we need to do is what they tell us, and all will be well. Even friends and family can join the 'you need to do' brigade. Going through illness and diagnosis with long-term conditions causes a shift on the axes.

The diagnosis itself can be like a lightening blow. Usually, it comes unannounced and even if we think we are prepared, we aren't. So, at a time when were unsure, shocked, confused, we open a door to an uninvited avalanche of 'shoulds' and 'at leasts!' You should do deep breathing, do exercise, eat more, eat less, you shouldn't work so hard, you should keep busy, you should/ or shouldn't take chemotherapy, you should/shouldn't take vitamins, turmeric, apple cider vinegar……. That's just some of the advice I've had. It's EXHAUSTING.

For me, not only was this exhausting but it also triggered shame – 'if I had only taken Vitamin D more consistently . . . Maybe it was the glass of wine I have with dinner that caused the cancer?'. This may link into earlier episodes of shame and cause a more extreme reaction of low mood or loss of esteem and confidence. Generally, others give 'advice' is with good intent, but the impact isn't good.

I wanted to be listened to, to be held, to be met with compassion. That was what made the biggest difference. I would ask for help or advice when the time was right, and the person was right.

When I was first diagnosed with breast cancer, my children were still in primary school. And in truth the first thing I experienced was guilt. My internalised message was *you must always be there for your family*. This guilt was unspoken and unexplored. It was tucked away like a cancer of a different kind. Consequently, when I was given unsolicited advice, it could trigger my sense of guilt and failure. Sometimes this advice was from healthcare professionals but might also be from family and friends.

Finding out who you are, and what your needs are, are fundamental to finding health and wellbeing in times of significant life-changes. Many conditions are manageable with good knowledge and the right motivators. But health professionals, informed by evidence from biomarkers, may make assumptions about what you should do to improve. Some of us may be able to take that on board immediately, but for many it will need a period of adjustment, and this may lead to tensions with health professionals.

This Element is therefore about understanding yourself. By widening your self-awareness you can respond with knowledge, and become able to ask the right questions to support your way of life and way of learning. It's not part of our culture to explore self- knowledge. Our education is cognitive based, so we learn about science, mathematics, history, English but rarely about internal processes or mental wellbeing. Other cultures may instil that learning from the home and school.

■ Mindfulness

Mindfulness is a practice that has crossed cultures. It borrows practices from Buddhist traditions but teaches it in a secular way. John Kabat Zinn[1] brought the practice to the Western world. He has done extensive research to prove its effectiveness in a culture whose healthcare believe system is evidence-based practice. Indeed, it could have been known as heartfulness, but it was felt this would potentially be rejected as being too unscientific. And so Mindfulness was born. It's a pivotal time for the adoption of Mindfulness practice, as more and more children are learning it in school. It relieves stress, improves behaviours and is fundamentally based in a practice of compassion. It can be seen as a

---

1 *Full Catastrophe Living*, Jon Kabat-Zinn (^ publisher? ^ date? ^page?)

form of stress-reducing cognitive behavioural therapy, but that diminishes its potential as a practice for life.

I trained in delivering the adult *Mindfulness for Life* course, which is much more interested in deepening understanding of the self, connecting body and mind, and integrating gratitude, kindness, and compassion into daily life. The course lasted a year and within that year my mother died. Not only that, but through the time of grieving, I was also losing my mobility. I have no doubt the practice and the group held me in a time of significant loss.

Through the mindfulness practice I knew, both somatically and psychologically, that I would get through it. Because of the work I do, I had already done work on self-knowledge, but I tended to focus on that at a cognitive level. This let me off the hook on the harder part, which is the 'knowing' in the body and engaging with the emotions. It was mindfulness practice that finally helped me with the deeper knowing. It helped me not be scared to lift the lid on the difficult emotions, as I didn't have to solve them or judge them, I just had to be alongside them, put an arm round them even, and just breathe. For someone who believes in cognitive learning, it was a big jump, but I eventually really welcomed it, when talking was no longer enough.

■ Mindfulness Practice

I'd suggest you try mindfulness practice to support you as you explore the other Elements; here are some thoughts and ideas on mindfulness practice.

You can start small with breathing practice if you prefer. An easy app to use is the Breathing App**. It starts you with, for example, a 5-minute breathing practice. With or without the app, you can try sitting upright (or lying if that easier for you) and breathe in through your nose (especially important during a flu season or pandemic as the small hairs in your nose are your first barrier against the virus) for 5 counts and out for 6 counts in a slow rhythm for five minutes.

This is not only pleasant - it also helps to settle the parasympathetic nervous system. This governs your stress reaction, and the breathing can settle that anxiousness in many of us. This pause in busy lives also helps us notice more. For example, to notice how you were at the start of the breath practice and then how you are afterwards. Did you notice anything different? What, if anything, came up for you? What were you curious about? These are all good mindful questions and can help you as you learn more about mindfulness. Should you wish to explore this further, there are many courses available, some online of course. They will all help you move forward and be valuable in this process of coming to know yourself, learning not only what you think you need but, with closer attention, what messages your body is delivering. The headache, the backpain, the stomach problems and so on all belie the oft repeated, 'I'm fine.'(In my world, the phrase, 'I'm fine' can cover anything from, 'I'm doing ok', to 'don't ask or you will regret it!') Mindfulness is often thought of as a relaxation technique, and it is extremely helpful for stress, but what it really is an awareness tool, for learning about how you react in all senses.

■ The Johari Window

There are many more ways to build awareness of yourself. The Johari Window[2] is a way to increase awareness of what others see in you, but you don't see in yourself. It is a tool that was developed by psychologists and is used in therapy and coaching. The window contains four sections which reflect four dimensions of self-knowledge. Using a process with trusted others it supports you to deepen self-awareness and is especially helpful to understand your strengths and bring to awareness some blind-spots.

The first time I did it, it was helpful to me. As someone with a strong 'must get it right' value, I always could see what I didn't do; what I was less good at. I try now to adopt a 'good- enough' approach but it's taken me years to get there. I kept this self- doubt inside, and others would not see it in the same way but when I got feedback- informally usually- I was pleasantly surprised. That was of course so important. Because someone like me (and maybe you) is at risk of trying to be the best

[2] *Of Human Interaction: The Johari Model,* Joseph Luft, 1969

cancer patient there is. I'm especially at risk of running myself ragged to be my version of best. With my first diagnosis it was that I was determined it wouldn't affect others so I tried to be the best wife I could, best mum, daughter, friend, colleague and of course nurse. This resulted in a tendency to respond to offers of help by saying, 'I'm fine!' I was so busy trying to be the 'good' cancer patient that I didn't know how to ask for help, and I didn't even know I needed it.

At that time there was a famous woman with secondary breast cancer (meaning it had spread to her bones and beyond) much in the media because she was running marathons. I looked at her I thought respect! And could just picture the words failure, written on my own t-shirt. I was done in. **Please, please, please media stop only telling tales of 'happy-clappy' cancer patients (or diabetes, or heart attack, etc . . .), because it leaves us ordinary folk feeling like failures. And frankly life is tough enough.**

The people who helped me then were the ones who dropped in food or took me for a coffee or lunch or a glass of wine. They listened through my crazy denial phase, they let me cry when I had nothing more to give and they gradually helped me let go of trying to pretend nothing had changed, and to let the door open a bit to allow some help.

What happened, too, was that people told me about the strength they noticed in me, that I hadn't noticed in myself. And that was so important because the more we recognise our strengths, the more we will be able to plot our way through a difficult time. I gradually learned what worked for me and what didn't and allowed myself to negotiate that to help me to a more balanced and healthy way to live. I'd retained a tendency to have a rant about what others needed to do to help me live and work (like kids picking up their clothes or putting away their laundry!). I did some 'talking therapy' briefly and the biggest thing I retained from that (and knew already - but only in relation to other folks!) was you can't change other people; you can only change how you are with them. Of course!

I was expending all this energy trying to get others to change or trying to fix things that weren't mine to fix. When I learned to stop doing that, it was such a revelation. I was less tired and less stressed. And changing how you act often itself creates change.

I'd love to say I always did that wisely and calmly but oh no, sometimes I had a tantrum. One I particularly remember was with my son. When I was collecting washing, I was regularly crawling all over to find socks, t-shirts, the works. And then I would put the clean laundry on his bed to be put away and it would stay there, often scooped up and dumped in the laundry again. So, one less than enchanted evening, I opened his bedroom door, saw the mess and to his astonishment I threw the pile of clothes across the room. I explained in a half yell, half cry that there was no point in me treating them well when he did that anyway. I suspect he improved slightly for a while. It didn't change much! He's still a bit messy his wife doesn't care because she's messy too. And you won't find better parents or people.

■ Reflections for professionals

Thank you for joining with us to work through this book. I imagine you will notice that its rather different from other books on self-management of long-term conditions or cancer or even COVID-19.

The chapter is based on the understanding that the more self-aware we are, the more we will engage in an authentic or real way with each other. It means we are less likely to project our own challenges and issues on to others or to work from a place of denial. I do believe denial has a particularly useful place at the beginning when we are first diagnosed with a serious condition. But if it becomes the only mechanism to help us cope there is a significant risk of not doing the behaviours that will improve outcomes and self-care in general.

The person who does amazingly well at the beginning may be working from denial. This may help them cope with a difficult start to long-term illness but it's crucial that the carers are aware and know it may be replaced by a frightening reality which has hitherto been avoided.

Each cancer diagnosis I've had, I have initially been quite high in my mood and maybe a little glib about how I was. It's always got me through. The first time it probably got me through till after my surgery. Attending radiotherapy, in waiting rooms full of brutal reality, was the treatment that burst my bubble. It made me recognise the seriousness and how my life was changing.

I have seen this too in people with diabetes when it can take several months for the reality to impact. (I call this the 'I've changed to diet coke in my vodka' stage). Its only when this stage passes that education programmes can help. As part of person-centred care, it is useful to check for denial. If you are finding resistance, then the best thing is not to push harder (the 'yes but's' are very evident here). 'What would help most just now?' is the best kind of intervention at this stage.

I recommend as you read through the book, you also complete the suggested exercises. Many of you will also live with long-term conditions or have had serious illness. We are all human and react to the world differently, including the world of healthcare. Hopefully this book will help you too, especially as COVID-19 has been a challenge for us all.

It may also be that you may want to recommend this book for others and so it's helpful to experience it. I suggest that you too keep a journal so you can reflect over time.

Element Two:
Understanding your values

This chapter is to help you be clearer about your personal values. If this is the first time you've ever thought of this, you may wonder why it matters. We all have values shaped by our experiences, from home and family as we grew up, from work colleagues, from studies and other learning, from those we love, but are often unaware of them. The reason it is valuable to bring them to awareness is that if our way of living is out of alignment with our values it will affect our mental wellbeing and ability to live as our best selves. As Ghandi put it,

'Happiness is when what you think, what you say and what you do are in harmony'.

Our values are likely to evolve over time, with different influences and experience, but essentially, they are a core part of us. Knowing your values will help you understand areas of stress and how best to tackle a serious and long-term condition. They can also help you seek out partners and friends. When people live their values in work and life it shows. Others notice it and value it: it's a kind of superpower.

▪ What Matters Most?

Reflect for a moment and consider who you know either personally as a leader or someone you experience at a distance like political leaders, who live and work their values. How do you respond or relate to them?

Can you identify what those values might be? You may even want to write them in your journal. We will look at several tools that can help you identify your values and once you have them you can record them in your journal and notice if they change over time. Do they resonate with your inner voice? And would you say that your life now is in harmony with them? Thinking back to the Gandhi quote, could you say that what you do, think, and speak does reflect those core values? This might how you express yourself in the world (congratulations) - but maybe some of those values sit deeply and are currently unexpressed?

For example, if someone with strong values of working hard and being successful is hit by serious illness, they may find it harder to adjust to an altered way of living. A diagnosis of covid-19 or cancer may often have long-term consequences as well as an acute phase. Both may lead to disability and significant change in wellbeing.

If freedom is a value, then being dependent on others will be especially stressful. However, if you have adaptability and gratitude as core values, you will have a greater ability to cope with major illness. Our values will often change over our lifetime, it's through experience and reflection on it. What's important at any point in time is that we understand more about how to reply, if some asks, 'What matters to you'?

Person-centred care is beginning to change how professionals approach working with people. The Institute of Healthcare Improvement in Boston (IHI)[3] first captured this way of framing person-centred care. It's best understood as instead of saying, "What's the matter with you" the clinician can say instead "What matters to you?" So rather than getting a list of symptoms you get a sense of the person and the context as well as what's troubling them.

We are all more than a clutch of symptoms, we are individuals, people not patients. So, when we are asked, what matters to us, unless we have thought of what truly is important to us, the risk is we miss the opportunity to go beyond the predictable. If you don't yet have a sense of what especially matters, you may miss the opportunity to ask for what could really help long-term.

---

[3] The Power of Four Words: 'What matters to you?' Institute of Healthcare Improvement www.ihi.org/What matters/Pages/default.aspx Improving Health and Health Care Worldwide | IHI - Institute for Healthcare Improvement

If core values to you are honesty and authenticity, then you will seek that in your health and care professionals, and won't hide anything from them, for example. If core values are about success, then getting back to work may be a priority. Your values can help you to shape your response to illness in a way that that accepts who you are and works with you from that place.

Without some self-knowledge, the question of what matters to you may indeed be hard to answer. Your mind may go blank (a common reaction what we are stressed). Or in that moment, you may only be able to think you want to go home. That's always my go-to answer! Even when I was struggling to move and had a boot on my broken leg I wanted to go home. However, I also knew it was important to me to work on my recovery and get the appropriate rehabilitation. I recognised the importance of getting home but I needed reassurance that I would have community support. I was prepared to dig my heels in. In consequence I got an excellent community physiotherapist who worked with me and gave me encouragement and courage to keep going.

Some hospitals now have boards, with charts to capture some of these key questions. Sadly, they are often left undone. Maybe the staff are too busy to do it – however, the time taken can save time in the long run. I would advocate: if it's not done by staff at home or in hospital, then don't be scared to do it yourself.

The follow-up question is, who matters to you? So often assumptions are made about who that will be. It's not always family – it could be a close friend, a pet, another health, or social care professional. It's worth giving that some thought and making sure you can express your needs.

The answers to the questions of who and what matters to you may well change over time, as situations and conditions change. For example, as a cancer progresses, it may require support for different internal and external resources may be required. The same is true for progressive diseases whose passage will be different for each of us. So, these are not fixed points, they need revisited.

■ Who are we?

So often we are known for the work we do, where we grew up, the school we went to, the family circumstance, the place we live, the car we drive, the clothes we wear, our accent, our skin colour . . . the list is endless. So are the judgements that sit alongside it. To really know yourself and to be at peace with that and to be able to celebrate that is so valuable. The work we have done so far on building self-knowledge can help you learn to sit with yourself in acceptance and in love. Building self-acceptance takes time and never ends, but meantime: breathe deeply, put back your shoulders and say, I know who I am, and I am good enough. Connect as you do that to your compassion for yourself, and others' compassion for you.

Not everyone has grown up with emotional literacy - it can often be counter cultural. Also, if you have cognitive challenges, they can affect your ability to express yourself. In times of depression or stress we also can lose articulacy. Some tools[4] have been developed to help – such as a set of cards which have both words and illustrations to match the feeling. Words such as: *heard, fortunate, hopeful, annoyed, satisfied, confused, glad, anxious, livid*. If communication is difficult then it may be worth getting a set so you can express how you feel. Also, you might want to read this book in a group or with another person who could aid your ability to get most from the experience.

I have a strong value of independence. And now I am increasingly dependent on others. Even as I write that I must breathe deeply. I forget at times and make plans for things that I can't do on my own. And don't get me started on the poor accessibility of our environment. I used to love to walk the dog, Cara, on my own, go to the beach, play with a ball, see her delight in running like the wind, faster than all the other dogs with her long lurcher's legs. Even with two of us, organising us both, holding onto scooters and fast dogs are not easy.

Just before Christmas 2019 Cara had a growth on her leg. It very quickly spread with infection; it was thought to be an aggressive cancer. Tests showed there was no spread and we found ourselves having to agree to her back leg being amputated. I cried in the vet hospital as I have never

[4] Emotional touchpoints | HIS Engage

cried for myself. It was the kind of sobbing that can't be held, the tears streamed and formed puddles down me. I was so distressed for her, and what we needed to do for her future. That day I cried tears for all of us: for Cara, for Andrew, for me. For lives changed for good.

Eventually I heard myself say, 'she will adapt, like me.' The loss of mobility for me was like other losses I had experienced, it never left however the pain lessened gradually. But some days, like that one, it feels as fresh and as sharp as ever. Thankfully, it was a foreign body and not cancer that invaded Cara's leg. And as all the vets predicted, she adapted very quickly. She remains the star of the beach, not only running but swimming too. We cut a scene when we head out, the 'hippie' Grannie on her mobility scooter, the three-legged dog and Andrew trying not to lose either of us.

■ Reflections for professionals

Understanding more about your own values will help you understand where your own bottom line is. Consider the Gandhi quote again: 'Happiness is when what you think, what you say and what you do are in harmony.' Would this apply to you? What do you think is out of alignment? Would you want or be able to balance it? Who could help you? What could be the first step in making that change?

The deeper understanding that you and others may work from different values could be helpful in working out how best to work together. This may be with your team but also with the people you support. Empathy has been described as walking a mile in another's shoes, and compassion, to be willing to walk alongside them on that path, however challenging. And that may be difficult if your values clash. This work can help you understand what is happening, and to recognise that you won't change others' values, but you can change how you choose to work with them.

A strong value that you hold may not be held by the person you are working with. If you hold a strong value of honesty, it might be difficult to understand the behaviour of someone with a strong value of pleasing people. They may tell you instead what you want to hear, rather than the tougher reality. When I moved from clinical care, where I worked with people with diabetes, to National Director of a Diabetes Charity (Diabetes UK), what struck me was that no one asked for help with controlling blood sugar. No, they wanted help with shift work, travel, special days like weddings. It was all about 'how do I live my life?', whereas 'what's my HbA1c'? would have been at the top of my agenda as a nurse.

Asking the question 'what matters to you?' can be so helpful. It enables you to work with a person's natural motivation. If at first the answer is more general, like 'family', you can go on to ask, 'what else?' or 'who else?', so can work out a care plan that's truly person-centred. Explore, too, what people want when receiving information - is it 'tell me it all upfront' or would they prefer it in little bites? Maybe it's 'give me time to chat it through' or 'give me leaflets' - or both! It may be to include their partner or not. 'Don't assume things' is always a good start! Working in this way builds trust in the relationship and greater ability to enable wellbeing in the future. This is such a satisfying way to work.

In any relational work,[5] just as with working with anyone with cancer, COVID-19 and other long-term condition, it's not important to know all the answers. But it is important to know the right questions.

With these reflections in mind-what matters to you in your practice now?

---

[5] *A Relational Approach to Therapy*, National Counselling Society. www.nationalcounsellingsociety.org

Element Three:
Understanding yourself

The focus of this chapter is 'What are your strengths?' If you want to try to identify them, I recommend you list them quickly without overthinking or censoring. How many did you get to? What does that tell you? Are you satisfied with what you wrote? Do you perhaps you tend to 'yes but?'

Can you accept a complement without qualifying it? Do you say thank you? Or maybe instead say: my hair is a mess, this old thing, it shows my big stomach, it's all make-up.......and so on. I've told them all at one time or other. But if you can smile and say, thank you, enjoying the compliment, it can really make your day.

Compliments don't come easily in our culture. At least not for my generation, and I know I still can struggle not to point out what's wrong instead of right. My Mum's idea of a compliment was 'your hair is much better like that!' It's not quite as uplifting as it was intended. You need to work quite hard to feel good about that kind of back-handed praise. Were you complemented as a child? Can you remember any complement you received? I can't. But maybe I didn't make it easy. I was a small dark haired wee Scottish girl who would only answer to Cheyenne Bodie,[6] a tall cowboy from a TV programme, who roamed from town to town, beating up bad guys. I've lost my Stetson hat but still occasionally feel drawn to fight the bad guys even if it's in my work or only in my blog.

[6] Cheyenne TV Series 'a physically large cowboy with a gentle spirit' en.wikipedia.org

Even at school the message was to strive to be the best, anything else wasn't good enough. It's very disheartening for most people who would never be the best in the class but were nonetheless working hard. When I worked as a nurse I gave a talk for a group of doctors, on how to support people, especially when they need to change behaviours. It seemed to go well. Later in the week, one of the GPs I worked with said, 'I heard you were very good the other night.' I felt myself glow. If only he had stopped there. 'Not like a nurse at all', he finished. The smile disappeared and I guess my response channelled my Cheyenne Bodie.

When I took on the post of National Director at Diabetes UK, I was quickly asked to speak on BBC TV news about some research that had been published. It was a pre-record and so I knew when it would be on. I thought, I will tell my Mum - she will be chuffed, maybe tell her friends? I phoned her up and explained I would be on at 8am on BBC Scotland. She hesitated and said 'oh, that is when my hairdresser comes, so I will miss it'. If I'm honest I was a bit surprised and hurt. I may even have indulged in a huff for a day or so. But with distance I could see it differently, firstly she didn't manage change easily after my dad died, and for her this was a step too far. Her family message of don't get above yourself, and don't put your head above the parapet, was too strong for this to be comfortable.

I found these messages to be in me too when I felt a bit vulnerable. The Imposter Syndrome was alive and kicking hard at times, especially in a national role. For me it might translate into I'm not good enough, especially in relation to men in senior roles. I found I carried a strong gender-based 'should'. Many of us, both men and women, still carry gender 'shoulds'. Sometimes these are so entrenched we experience them as givens. So why this focus on 'shoulds'? If your list of shoulds is small, that's great, well done. But it's helpful to just notice if they creep into your conversation. Shoulds tend to reflect other people's assumed agenda or expectations. We tend to carry them heavily on our shoulders. One of the most powerful sentences I read when I was exploring mindfulness was,

You are not your thoughts

The discovery that shoulds are constructs and are not reality was releasing. I realised when I was most stressed and feeling pressure, it was probably linked to a series of these shoulds. For example, when trying to meet a deadline even when it is impossible, I'd think, 'I shouldn't let people down'. That could lead to 'I'm a failure', "or 'I will disappoint them'. And so it went, causing real damage to my wellbeing. I've learned to control this over the years but there are still some situations where I can be triggered.

The Work[7] by Byron Katie has a worksheet called 'Judge your Neighbour'. The approach is to flip your thinking on an issue and trick your brain into allowing that other perspectives might be true. Once your brain has challenged. The relief attached to accepting a different way of seeing your world, can be so powerful, even life changing. It can release so much energy trapped in trying to hold the situation. If you have a situation, you feel stuck with, that causes you sleepless nights or distress, making you go over and over it, I suggest you try the 'Judge your Neighbour' worksheet. First, watch some of the videos on her website so you can get the most from it. Maybe even work through it with a trusted friend.

So, before we move on, the next time you recognise your thoughts are populated with shoulds, step back for a moment and simply ask yourself 'Is it true'?

■ What is wrong with you?

When I did my nursing degree, we learned about the 11 systems of the body - what was normal in the respiratory, circulatory, nervous, cardiovascular system etc., and how it might go wrong. Medicine and nursing is often still taught in that way. We learned about what goes wrong. Honestly, I found it fascinating. It's not all we learned of course. One of our lecturers, Dr Alison Tierney, had worked on the ADL assessment (activities of daily living), developing Roper-Logan-Tierney model of nursing.[8] This was the start of nursing assessments. We did learn about communication styles, active listening, and empathy as well.

[7] *The Work*, Byron Katie www.thework.com.
[8] Roper-Logan-Tierney's Model for Nursing Based on a Model of Living - Nursing Theory (nursing-theory.org)

And off we went into the world, well prepared in many ways and not at all in others. We especially didn't learn about health, simply ill-health, we didn't see people holistically and especially not people who existed within a complex social and political system. It's a tough ask but necessary as none of us exist out of a context of family, community and nation.

We were trained to assess what was wrong and what were the deficits in the activities of daily living. It's been a way of working for decades, the doctor as a kind of detective looking for a culprit (*Sherlock Holmes* was written by a doctor). And in an emergency, it works well. You find out what's wrong and fix it. But with much of modern healthcare that will not be the case. Hippocrates himself recognised 'it's much more important to know what person the disease has than the disease the person has'. So many with the experience and impact of serious and long-term illness can find themselves adrift from diagnosis, when the reach and focus of modern medicine is stuck on finding the villain! And if you have an issue that can't be diagnosed, it can lead to the person (and sometimes the medic too) feeling they've failed, rather than turning it around and asking, well what can you do, and focusing on supporting that.

When I met that situation myself, I realised eventually that I would have to shore up my strengths to recover. The most striking example of this for me was when I was slowly recovering from spinal surgery. In June 2018, by the time of surgery, I was rapidly losing mobility and living with increasing nerve pain. I almost died after haemorrhaging in theatre. I was in ITU for 5 days and then HDU for another 10 days. In all I was in hospital for a month, including breaking my leg! I was exhausted and only inched forward in my recovery. I held the fear in my body which I think was mainly linked to my times in ITU. It's common to have a form of post- traumatic stress disorder after time in ITU and so I was processing this slowly as well.[9]

With the love and support of my family and good friends alongside good support from my GP and a skilled and compassionate physiotherapist, I got to near Christmas and thought, next year will be better. But I had needed a CT scan for a post-operative issue, and it found an unrelated, but significant cancer in my previously unaffected breast. I was stunned and my usual resilience was lost to me. 'I'm

---

[9] https://www.thelancet.com/journals/lanpsy/article/PIIS2215-0366(19)30031-8/fulltext#:~:text=The%20epidemiology%20of,L%20Fisher%2C%20PhD

broken', were my words to a doctor who is a friend. He listened as I said I didn't know if I had the fight for this, or the strength: 'should I just give in?'. These were the things I couldn't say to family. I was 25 years after my first cancer diagnosis, and now I faced the fourth, honestly, I was ready to give up. As I sat for a few weeks with the decision on what to do, I learned for the first time that I am a BRCA 2 gene mutation carrier. In some ways this was a relief as it made sense of the four diagnoses previously. It also meant a I needed a mastectomy for sure and removal of my ovaries.

I sank a little further. I took a few days on retreat in Cumbria. And I took the opportunity to self-reflect, regain strength with rest and good organic food. I found, in time, the will to keep going. I no longer focused on dying, I focused on living. With meditation I recalled the power of staying in the moment. A focus on things passed can trigger low mood or depression, and a focus on the future can become a source of anxiety - but in truth we only have the here and now.

Probably my stubbornness is my super skill. When I was able to focus, Mindfulness was extremely helpful. When that escaped me, my distraction was listening to audiobooks. Concentrating enough to read was at that time impossible for me. My husband, children and new grandson Davie formed a band of love around me; I was supported by my sister, wider family, and amazing friends. And there was always Netflix and an accompanying white wine!

Over that time my therapist at the retreat helped me explore what I really wanted, and it became clear to me I wanted to live. I was able to identify what would support me internally and externally.

Some key questions helped with that process:

① What have you drawn on to date to help you?

② What are you good at?

③ What have you learned so far that you can apply to this situation?

④ What are your strengths you can apply to this time and place?

These questions can lead to single answers, and if this happens, ask yourself then: "what else?" Slowly I found the strength to get through and to plan special times before and after my mastectomy. I carefully squirreled away memories. We were approaching Christmas 2019 with the plan we would make 2020 special - well, it certainly was memorable!

Super skills aren't usually the huge things, but they matter. Your skill might be researching about your condition. It may be that you are the person who really listens to people. Perhaps it's doing the quiz in the paper or being the person, everyone wants in the team for the family quiz. It may be to make people laugh or cry - or both. It may be knowing when to ask for help. Or letting go of perfection and settling for good enough. Perhaps it's practising gratitude and feeling burdens shift a little?

It may be useful to come back to these four questions over time because as life goes on your awareness changes. If you feel able you could create a small card, or postcard, and write down your current strengths on it. Compare this to your first list. Be curious about the changes.

Completing this chapter has hopefully helped shift from a deficit-based system (what's wrong with you) to an asset based one, what your strengths are. It's a big shift in how we do things normally, but the difference really releases energy to move forward.

Reflections for professionals
What are your strengths?

If someone asks you, you might list your achievements, where you are in a hierarchy, length of years in the profession and so on. How much does that tell you about strengths? To have worked in health and social care at the time of the 2020 pandemic, you will no doubt have enlisted all your strengths to keep going. Can you recognise them?

When met with patients who had struggled with awful symptoms without relief, Dr Reilly, a very skilled colleague of mine who worked in integrative medicine, would sometimes say 'how are you not dead yet?'.

Although said kindly, this was a deliberately shocking question that honoured how difficult it had been for them, and that they had enlisted huge strengths to get to this point in time. No longer seen as a victim of the condition, they were respected for speaking their own truth; and rather than a tick list of symptoms, they were connected to what they could do. To finally be heard like this can often lead to huge emotional release.

'Shoulds' are also so often associated professions; nurses should be selfless, physiotherapists should strong, doctors should know everything, social workers should be left wing! None of them should get ill themselves or have any needs. Those shoulds can trap people in the professions in over-working or ignoring their own needs.

Those we work with will be faced with many of these 'shoulds' - such as how cancer patients should be inspiring and courageous. With cancer, and I see it with Covid-19 patients too, the use of war analogies (having 'fought hard' and 'won battles') creates a narrative about the ones who survive - so by implication, those who die just haven't tried hard enough. People with Type 2 diabetes are constantly judged, a series of shoulds greeting the person on their diagnosis. These shoulds can contribute to a sense of overwhelm, and they take no account of the process of grieving for their former lives that patients need to go through. Instead of a list of shoulds, using a 'what matters to you just now' approach can help, due to its immediate focus. Perhaps it's to keep their driving licence so they can pick up their grandchild from school, or perhaps it's to cure a long-term infection. Maybe it's to feel better, less tired or to finally tackle their diet. Listening and supporting them is the strong foundation of a trusted relationship and a route to becoming true partners in care.

When working with people with chronic pain, the first suggestion from a clinician might be, 'you need to lose weight'. Without knowledge of that person's situation focusing on weight can deliver a final blow, or a break trust that the clinician will be able to help them. Weight gain is hugely complex. For example, I can hardly walk now, and I take two tablets that contribute to weight gain. I've lost so many other things with losing my mobility and having endless surgery for cancer: I need to be able to enjoy my food. My self-image is fragile, and a mention of weight gain would be so damaging. We know now that obesity, especially morbid (yes, isn't that a terrible description) obesity, is often linked to trauma, as are other conditions. The ACE study[10] showed that the risk of developing serious illness rose with the number of adverse childhood events someone experienced. And that it wasn't only mental health issues, it was also things like cancer, heart disease, strokes and of course obesity. So rather than a lecture, a question along the lines of 'what happened to you' can allow that person to acknowledge and speak their truth. Talking it out can improve someone's life.

Professionals in health and social care have been found to have higher ACEs than the general population so we ourselves can be triggered by situations that relate to our own histories. First of all, we need support when triggered and need not to feel judged. When we have processed our own vulnerabilities, we are then able to recognise the 'wounded healers' within ourselves - a strength that we hold, that can enable a deep empathy and compassion in our practice.

And your strengths will show themselves in many ways: the person who keeps everyone smiling, the person who praises appropriately, the kindness of a touch, the skill of experience, the enthusiasm of a recruit, the listener, the cool head in a crisis, the experienced diagnostician, the visionary, the completer/finisher, the organiser etc. Your strengths will sustain you when times are challenging. The pandemic, when too many times professionals were both patient and practitioner, reinforced that we are human beings, both strong and vulnerable. And a key strength is knowing when to ask for help. I've rarely met a health or care professional who wants to be described as a hero, but they do want the equipment and support to do their work and to be recognised and rewarded for their skills. They also share a need to feel the warmth of human kindness when times are tough.

Maybe the best strength all of us can have is to make time to listen and to respond with compassion. This opens the possibility of improved wellbeing for all of us.

---

[10] The Relation between Adverse Childhood Experiences and Adult Health: Turning Gold into Lead. VJ Felliti,MD Ncbi.nlm.nih.gov

Element Four:

Find out who and what lifts you up and brings you joy

This Element is at heart about relationships. Understanding which ones will help you get through, and which will not, and why, is not always as you'd expect when facing serious and long-term conditions. Perhaps you find it strange to devote a whole section to this, but as the impact of other people can be devastating or life enhancing, it's important to distinguish the two.

So, I'm going to tell you a story about my first diagnosis with cancer. I was working as a nurse at our local practice. I knew lots of people and several I would call friends. It hadn't been so long since I had supported a friend through cancer treatment and was so glad to have been able to help. It's what you do, at least that what I have found. Sometimes it's not a great deal, but you do something, don't you? Just something that says: I'm alongside you.

It was the summer holidays, and my close friends were away, my father was seriously ill with cancer and my Mum was stressed and fearful for us both and lived over 80 miles away. I felt a strong need to protect them, and my sister who was busy with more family illness, her job and was several hundred miles away. My children were young, and my strong instinct was to protect them as well. I didn't lie but was very reassuring and positive I would recover and be well. My husband was working long hours and stressed of course. I was super woman, doing it all. It was exhausting…….

When I was diagnosed I let some people who were around know, waiting to tell my other friends until after their holiday. I heard nothing. People I thought were friends disappeared. I thought maybe I had offended them. Maybe they were just busy? I will admit to going over it in my head many times. School returned and I thought, I will hear from them now. Mmmm, no. Then one woman turned up to drop my son off, I think. I can't remember clearly but I remember her words. She asked how I was. Fine, I said, not wishing to say more as I felt a loss of trust suddenly. And then she said, 'how does it feel to be on the other side?' I felt like she had slapped me. 'Not good', I said and smiled as I closed the door. And vowed to stay well clear of her in the future. I wondered if I had patronised her previously when she asked me about health issues? What had I done to have invited such callousness? She made me wary of others and so I was careful who I spoke to. But others just slid away.

But that isn't the whole story. I took the other disappearances and rejections as being about me. Maybe illness had made boring, selfish, ugly....? I was truly hurt. But other people supported me, some I would not have expected. I was moved by their thoughtfulness and kindness. I tried to ignore the others.

Then fourteen years later, I was in my first few weeks as the Director of Breakthrough Breast Cancer in Scotland. I was well informed generally about the clinical aspects of breast cancer and my lived experience, but I thought it important to attend a conference on Living with Cancer. There was a session on something like the top ten things that were difficult when living with cancer. As I read the slide I froze. I was no longer the objective observer, I was Audrey, still living with cancer and realising I was not alone in being hurt by people disappearing from my life. In fact, it was an issue for most people. It was high up on the list! My body flooded with relief. It wasn't me. What triggers it - who knows? A fear of death, cancer and illness, unresolved issues of their own or maybe these relationships weren't friendships. Maybe I was merely useful. My value of helping people had created imbalance in some relationships. I learned from this and chose friends with more awareness. If a relationship was more about helping someone, then I did that with clarity. It saved me pain and distress. I share this as it's not just about cancer, it can be applicable in any serious illness. I share this so that others may recognise the syndrome. For some it may be members of their family who back off. Of course, family relationships are complex and it's only in the movies when everyone becomes wise and kind. Stress can bring out all our defence mechanisms and trigger difficult family dynamics. We all have them. and often family are not the people who will give the best support. It maybe it's just raw and painful for them, and sometimes they can't be who you want them to be. But maybe they could have a role that allows them to help as and when they are able.

But the biggest message in this is, it's not about you. It's their reaction to the situation.

It maybe be challenging but I would invite you to see them with compassion and let go of your expectations of them. Because the good news is that others step up instead, and that too is a common experience. People come forward with compassion and listen to you, respond to your needs, write cards, bring flowers, cook a meal, babysit, take you to appointments and importantly support your family too. I struggled with getting help and found it hard to ask. But I also learned by enabling people to help, helped them as well.

I have often thought, had I not been so unwell, I would never have known how loved I was. I grew up in a part of the world where we show our love with food. Sometimes it might be gifts . . . but don't spoil them, mind! Generally, we don't say 'I love you' easily - well, not in public. However, illness can unleash emotional communication. A hold of the hand, a hug, a kiss, warm words are all the best medicine. The experience of the pandemic has confirmed the importance of human contact. Those who offer their love in whatever way are so valuable to our wellbeing.

I learned that those who bring you joy - who energise you, build your confidence, improve your mood exponentially - are often not those you would expect. But out of these experiences, special friendships emerged. When you hear or say the words 'there are more good than bad people' in the world, it is them you think of. So often they may not realise the difference they are making. They can also allow a mutuality that means when they have a need, you can help them too.

I've never agreed with sayings like 'cancer is a gift'. The triteness makes me angry. I've wondered if it lets people of the hook, helps them feel better and believe distress is in the past. But it's unfair to the true experience. Perhaps there are positives for some of us, but it can never be a whole truth. And these comments can make it harder for people to own the pain of their personal experience, be it physical or emotional. I'm always tempted to want to take pain away from others. But the best thing we can do is encourage and allow people to talk - and if they don't want to talk, to accept that that's ok too.

Reflections for professionals

This Element is perhaps different from the others, but we are people who too become ill, become informal carers and so on and we can find ourselves with friendships where we feel let down. I'm fortunate to have many friends who are doctors, nurses, and support workers. They are great friends, skilled, thoughtful, and kind. And like me they have been on a journey to ensure they can look after themselves in relation to caring for others. Social work-based organisations have recognised the need for supervision, not in the managerial sense but as a built-in source of support and personal and professional development. Nursing has occasionally toyed with this, but I've not heard of is approach imbedded in practice to date. GPs in training have a similar process. It's a powerful learning tool which recognises that the healing process is a relational one. Supervision for all the caring professions would be a hugely valuable role and may prevent burnout and loss of skilled people who feel unvalued.

Professionals can be at risk of having friends who are takers - energy sappers, whose need takes up the oxygen in the room. When I'm well I'm able to see this, accept it as is and knowingly give my support. But as my energy has declined with illness, I recognise that my balance of friends has changed. I'm told I do still support my good friends and I'm incredibly grateful for that.

Those of you working in caring roles, check who brings you joy in your life. And who doesn't. Are your needs being met in this relationship? Awareness helps you know what to nurture and what to let go of.

In addition, as professionals, it's important to recognise if this pattern is affecting us too. Coaching helps to process especially when we are feeling stuck. *We also need nurturing loving relationships.*

Element Five:

Working with your health and social care team as a partner in care

The spectacular tribute to the NHS at the 2012 Olympic opening ceremony showed the esteem held and the love we have for the NHS. It's almost a spiritual connection and use of words like 'angels' in connection with it hints further at this. An obsolete *Call the Midwife* type world also affects the understanding our modern relationships with NHS workers. During the pandemic we were called on to 'clap for carers' and then for 'heroes', evoking assumptions about invincible super-heroes. I am eternally grateful for the NHS - my ill-health would have had a huge financial impact in many parts of the world. And I have met many health and social care workers who have gone beyond the everyday for me and for my family. I initially clapped for them but then saw the irony of politicians clapping and yet not following lockdown guidance or law. I clapped initially, with the politicians who promised pay rises and delivered nothing. I clapped, but then said, what about us, we've followed the rules, my husband is my carer and is in an age category that is higher risk for coronavirus and for all that, we've had no support. We all need acknowledgement for our contribution. But I'm sorry but I'm not holding out for a hero: I want a skilled, informed partner in my care who listens to me, respects my opinion and a situation where we seek solutions together, and speak honestly through the difficult times. And who really wants to be a hero? Many of the so-called heroes understandably say they don't to be heroes; they want decent pay and proper investment in services.

Successful outcomes in care for long-term conditions and serious illness result from respectful partnerships. The superpower here is great listening and communication skills. It's mutual respect, too, but these qualities often aren't valued in very hierarchical institutions and cultures like medicine and nursing. Modern health and social care is about team work, where each member of the team is valued and has an equal voice.[11] Atul Gwande has spoken convincingly on this topic, backed up by the evidence that the safest team is one that values all voices, and increasingly it's recognised that the 'patient' is part of that team.

The world of matrons ruling hospitals is gone; the world of consultants dishing out orders at the end of the bed is not completely gone and not all the behaviours have changed. Those of us living with long-term conditions may not always like the change either. Some maybe preferred a time when we thought it was up to others to make us better. We've lived through an era when pharmaceuticals have extended exponentially. The baby boomers and those who came after learned that there was a pill that fixed anything. Mary Poppins sang about that spoonful of sugar helping the medicine go down and we gladly swallowed it. Pharmaceutical companies are some of the richest companies in the world. In earlier times, they bombarded doctors with gifts, and conferences in beautiful places, to show the efficacy of their research. These practices have rightly been stopped in the UK but it remains the case that the focus on evidence-based practice is swayed by what research is funded. Most of the evidence sits with the pharma companies and so the evidence base for treatment is usually for drugs. Getting NHS funding for education programmes, peer support development or behaviour change work has been exceedingly difficult. Even when research is done and found to be effective with the people-based programmes, the quality of the evidence is questioned. The result is a reliance on medicines over self-management support. In conditions like diabetes the importance of education alongside medication has finally been accepted. Insulin as therapy was developed by pharmaceutical companies and stopped Type 1 diabetes being a fatal disease. Now after many years of research and lobbying, education

---

11 "The Checklist Manifesto" Atul Gwande 2009

programmes are funded for both Type 1 and 2 diabetes. For many conditions the answer will lie with both medication and peer support.

Before the pandemic in Scotland, Catherine Calderwood was Scottish Government Chief Medical Officer. She introduced the concept of Realistic Medicine. This has a particular focus on shared decision making and a personalised approach to care. No longer a case of 'doctor / nurse knows best', but a decision made through conversation, with a shared risk, taken with knowledge.

When I was diagnosed with a spinal growth, I was the most shocked I've been in my life. I had been in denial about the seriousness and had tried every self-care approach I could find. At the appointment with my surgeon, he said my condition meant that I would end up unable to move my legs and lose control of my bladder and bowel function, I couldn't believe it. After that first appointment I developed amnesia. Fortunately, my husband was with me. The neurosurgeon offered to see us anytime, so I returned a week later with questions, especially about options. He couldn't offer any written information as the condition was quite rare. Dr Google would need to be consulted, I thought. There was little but what there was confirmed what the neurosurgeon had said.

I had to decide whether to opt for surgery, or to wait and see. I also paid for a second opinion which confirmed the first. I chose to wait and see. What can I do meantime? I asked the neurosurgeon. The answer was nothing! I was actively involved with the development of the self-management strategy and was not going to accept that answer. Don't fall or do contact sports, he added. What could I safely do to help my muscle power I asked. Finally, he understood that I wasn't thinking I could cure the growth another way - rather, I needed to do something that optimised the time I had. I was referred to hydrotherapy which helped me regain some confidence and I walked up and down the local pool with grim determination. As the next months passed, I conceded that surgery was inevitable.

That experience confirmed for me that there is always something you can do, and that saying 'nothing' is so disabling. I think the surgeon learned that too. Information is king with a diagnosis of serious or long-term illness. But it needs to be appropriate and accessible and given from a person-centred perspective. In many situations all the information is imparted at the first appointment. Often people are too traumatised to take things in, and this overwhelms them. Timely information is key, in bite sized chunks and aimed at answering 'what matters to you?'. Our understanding of how our body works is hugely variable and we process information differently. Ensure you have someone with you at your initial appointments at least. Ask them to take notes or record on your phone with permission. The Realistic Medicine policy of Scottish Government suggests five questions to ask when you are considering treatment. I have used them to good effect.

1. Is this test, treatment or procedure really needed?

2. What are the benefits and downsides?

3. What are the possible side effects?

4. Are there simpler or safer options?

5. What would happen if I did nothing?

Often these will come up in discussion but having a check list helps ensure clarity.

Chemotherapy is a good example of the need for these questions. The risk/benefit assessment is complex, and patients can feel compelled to take chemo without questioning when a team of doctors are recommending it. Once the tumour is graded, then a recommendation of treatment is made. As personalised medicine (e.g., genotype mapping) improves with targeted treatments, chemotherapy will be tailored and appropriate. Just now we don't always know who really needs it and this can lead to over treatment with toxic medication. I would encourage you to be sure you know all the options and the risk versus benefit before making up your mind. We all have different relationships with risk, and these are complex concepts, and the decision needs to be based on the principle of informed consent.

An area I haven't touched on so far is the situation when someone has troubling symptoms but no diagnosis. The route to treatment and support through the NHS is through a diagnosis. Where there is none, there is a tendency to not believe the symptoms or to look for mental health causes. Consider how those with CFS (chronic fatigue syndrome) or ME (myalgic encephalitis) were treated before it was agreed that they are neurological illnesses. They were often diagnosed and treated for depression, which both carried stigma, and resulted in a failure to seek other treatment. The level of disbelief could be devastating to someone who was already feeling dreadful.

Chronic pain may often not have a diagnosis of a cause, and consequently may be poorly controlled (And there's the 'it is all in your head type of judgment' to deal with as well). It's hard to be a partner in your own care if no condition is identified. Self-esteem and efficacy are so damaged - as is the relationship with the doctors and the wider team. To challenge a lack of a care pathway or even an understanding of your symptoms takes courage. Many charities[12] and advocacy groups have been created to meet that gap and to search for support outside of traditional medicines. It can be life-changing to be really heard, especially by someone who has been through a similar experience.

Developing coping strategies like meditation is often hugely helpful for stress and anxiety. Pilates and yoga can help with pain, mobility, and building strength and balance. They can also help connect with a community of peers who are struggling. Other treatments like massage, reiki or reflexology can all improve fatigue, pain, and relaxation. This is not an exhaustive list by any means and the greatest help maybe doing a course in self-management, often targeted to your condition. Information is not only power, but the key to confidence in managing your own condition and being more in control of your health and well-being. And remember just because someone can't diagnose a condition, it doesn't mean that your symptoms aren't real. Learning assertiveness skills for consultations can help you to be clear about what you want.

Living with long-term conditions is about accepting your reality and finding your inner resources and the help beyond medicine. The experience is not a consistent one and for most of us it's up and down.

[12] About Self Management - Self Management and Co-Production Hub (alliance-scotland.org.uk)

Coming to an acceptance of what you can and can't do is crucial, especially if you focus on what you can do, and can even be life changing. Finding the right clinicians is an important aspect of successful outcomes - they need to be good listeners and accept your role as the expert in your own condition. But don't wait for miracles - open your mind as to possibilities about what else might help you feel better. Who would have believed the popularity of wild swimming before the pandemic?

■ Reflections for professionals

Depending on your role, the concept of the person as a partner may be surprising and even threatening. Using Realistic Medicine[13] as a guide and seeking new consultation techniques can be helpful. NHS Education Scotland (NES) is a valuable resource. Learning and using coaching skills for deep listening, checking understanding, exploring possibilities, and planning and enabling action are all essential components of working in partnership.

Working in this way engages the patient's innate motivation. Finding what matters to them, and supporting them to pursue that, is central. People have been found to choose less treatment for themselves than doctors suggest. Echoing this, doctors choose less treatment for themselves than they want for their patients, even when the guidelines say differently. The following are five questions from Realistic Medicine and are a valuable approach to shift the dialogue.

(1) Is this test, treatment or procedure really needed?

(2) What are the benefits and downsides?

(3) What are the possible side effects?

(4) Are there simpler or safer options?

(5) What would happen if I did nothing?

[13] Realistic Medicine – Shared decision making, reducing harm, waste and tackling unwarranted variation

Working in this way is potentially energising for both the individual and the clinician. When many of us were trained we were seen as the experts who shared their decisions, and the public did what they were told (or not). Moving to an approach of shared expertise is vastly different and people need support for this change.

Element Six:

Learning and support from people with lived experience

This support (alongside traditional support) is an important part of understanding how to live well with cancer, serious illness, and long-term conditions: adjusting to living with a new condition is never easy, especially if it results in feeling lonely and isolated. You are in a new landscape and those around you can't really join you there. Indeed, they are in their own new place and need to adjust, grieve and re-orientate.

When I first had breast cancer I was only in my thirties. But I had a friend, Moira, who had recently completed treatment and was getting on with her life. I was so reassured by that. We spoke regularly and managed lunch or coffee. We shared experiences of drug treatments. Tamoxifen was a shared demon! I'd just been prescribed it and she was telling me about it. I remember the twinkle in her eyes, full of mischief as she pointed out I would get 'more' hairs on my chin. It was a 'what the ****' moment for me but in truth the least of my issues and we knew this. We fell about laughing, nonetheless. Around that time, I was offered information about a support group. I declined. Moira was all the help I needed just then. I was also worried as a local nurse working in the medical practice, concerned I would meet patients and struggle with boundaries. There was probably some denial too, but I did feel I needed some privacy, never easy for care workers in a small town. This was 26 years ago, so there was no Dr Google or online groups. I read a lot, and being in the middle of a Master's degree in public health, I had access to research. I contacted the charity Breast Cancer Care but chose not to take up their offer of help through peer support. The leaflets from the hospital were for older women. I reacted to them badly. To be fair, this was probably displaced anger and denial, but I clearly remember considering tearing it up and threading it through the grill on the 10th floor window. What stopped me was not wanting to look completely unhinged (even though at that time I probably was . . .)

We are generally so vulnerable at these times that it's rare that a leaflet will serve our needs. If the information is diverse and appropriate, then perhaps it will be useful back up. Ideally, though, we want to hear from someone we can connect with. I have sought support from several other charities since then. Maggie's Cancer Care[14] has given me such support. The sense of welcome and shared experience has grounded and soothed me.

The first time I went I hesitated, as I knew the team from my work and what I found was I needed personal one-to-one support. The nature of the work was high profile and constantly demanding both physically and emotionally. I was slowly realising that my health would not improve until I left the full-time role and had less travel to London. The irony of all of this made the pain and loss quite hard to bear. The support from Maggie's at the time helped me focus on my needs and travel the complex internal journey to a huge decision. After that I joined their meditation group and did tai-chi for a time until my spine couldn't cope. More recently I did a creative writing course and I gained so much from that. Writing helps me process how I feel. The wisdom, compassion and shared pain of that group gave me the support I didn't think I needed. The group was gently led, and we cried and laughed together as well as improving our writing skills. We were all ages and stages and learned from each other.

I had seen this in other situations. When I worked in diabetes, I witnessed the relief in parents of children with Type 1 diabetes when they met other parents at support days. They grew in confidence and let other people take responsibility for their children. I usually worked with

---

[14] www.maggies.org

the parents who gained new knowledge and explored shared issues in groups. And the children had fun! One day, we were ending. The group were discussing their fears so openly and movingly - I shed many a tear on those days. Suddenly we heard screams and held our breath until the screams became laughter. We gathered at the window and saw groups of children in waterproofs being hosed down to get mud off them. They had set off with snacks and glucose tablets, attended by medics and other volunteers, and enjoyed a muddy challenge course whilst also learning about managing hypos and safe risk-taking. The learning for all of them was massive. It could not have happened in another way.

Many charities and local groups offer a diverse range of learning opportunities. These include new activities that help with wellbeing and offer self-management support generally, working with peers as well as facilitated by people from the charity itself. Their value is immense, but too many people don't know this support is available. Too often there are ambivalent relationships between NHS workers and the charity/voluntary sector. I've seen free leaflets and posters lie unused in boxes within a GP surgery. This is undoubtedly multi-faceted: some practitioners will assume they are enough and guard their relationships. Other issues can be a lack of trust of the sector e.g., confusing the meaning of voluntary with amateur or unskilled. The evidence based/randomised control research is too often seen as the only evidence that counts, forgetting that lived experience and practice-based evidence also provides vital information for individuals and services and should be respected. These social models of disability-informed care services are offered alongside the medical model of care. The best experience for people is when the teams work together with mutual respect for each other's expertise.

There is also online information. I've seen many people urged not to google conditions and symptoms. It's a bit like telling the tide not to come in, it's such a natural thing to do now. What's most helpful is to suggest good websites and what you might want to avoid, to be helped to learn how to judge credibility. Depending on learning preference or reading confidence, videos may be an additional good source of information.Check for sites that are approved by the NHS, or those suggested by professional teams and charities with the resources to ensure the validity of the information they are sharing.

Essentially this Element is about self-management. Of course, this starts with more familiar advice about staying well, being active, eating well and sleeping well. But these can be forgotten in the maelstrom that is a new diagnosis.

With most diagnoses, all of us will go through something allied to a cycle of grieving. At the time of diagnosis, we can be at any point in that cycle. Consequently, our needs will differ. Speaking to others with the condition helps us realise we aren't alone in our reactions. We might be able to share fears about the future, how will it map out, what to expect and so on. But it's also there to talk about worries like jobs, relations, going out again, life and death. Those strangers can hear the fears we protect our friends and family from. I've been the person who has said, 'I won't tell things in a group with strangers.' How wrong I was. I've had great compassion and understanding from people who have only passed through my life for a short time. I do hope I've been able to help them too.

Too often people aren't aware of support groups or other offers like training in self-management or mindfulness. And it may only take connecting with one to have that sense friendship and of co-support. Since the pandemic so much information is online and that's invaluable. But we are human beings who need connection and unless there is a clinical or public health need, we should be helped to find relational solutions.

If that is difficult, say if you live in a in a small or remote community, finding a blog or podcast might offer the lived experience which is honest and, alongside some difficult truths, also remind you that life will continue, and a form of normality will be possible. When I was diagnosed with the spinal growth, I asked for information, and none existed. This was a rare condition, you see. There were no specialisms, no special nurses, or physiotherapists to guide your pathway. The contrast between this and a breast cancer diagnosis and treatment pathway were stark. In the case of the spinal growth I only had the neurosurgeon who was exceptionally thoughtful and kind and generous with his time but had no answer to so many of my questions.

He said not to google it. Mmmmm. It's the first thing I did of course, and nothing reassured me. Dr Google can be perilous. It reaffirmed my treatment options and the serious risk but said nothing about what that meant. Phrases like 'you would end up in a wheelchair' (this was also part of the explanation about potential outcomes given to me) are so laden. And what I found was I didn't hear anything else. I'm sitting in a wheelchair as I write this and frankly it's not the worst thing. For me, the pain is the worst. I discovered my best friend was water, hydrotherapy, and the local pool too.

That spring I was to be found walking up and down the pool. Hydrotherapy gave me the confidence and knowledge to go forward myself. As my condition worsened, my goal shifted from maximising my mobility, to improving my fitness for surgery once I'd made the difficult decision to have it. I went for surgery as fit as I could be. My message is don't be put off, find something you can do and enjoy that sense of control over your situation and improved wellbeing.

Wellbeing comes from many things, like diet, physical activity, connection with others, and from creative activities like writing, painting, jigsaws, music. If you are able, perhaps volunteering for the cause could be therapeutic. That may change over time, for example moving from fundraising to peer support or activism. The potential is huge: chat it through and plan. But remember it is ok just to be peaceful. Meditation and mindfulness might help with this but so might a good book, a favourite piece of music or a walk.

With each challenge I've faced there has been someone with experience of the issue to learn from. With the spinal growth and injury that has been invaluable. There is so little written on it, but I've had practical support, from encouragement to apply for personal independence payment (PiP), and where to get a low weight wheelchair, to being able to say, "this is shit". There are no specialist nurses or evidenced-based pathway for my condition, so a colleague, Linda, has helped me navigate the system and kept my head above water when the waves were threatening to overpower me. If you get the chance, do speak to others and be willing to take their help.

There are always downsides of course. If you have a life-limiting problem and are part of a support network, you will also be alongside others approaching end of life. For most of us, we are facing our worst fears. As part of a blogging network, I have been alongside people as they are dying. It's so hard to grieve for someone you haven't met but has touched your soul with their generous writing about their own truth. You may have exchanged words that have stayed with you, and grieved together for another fellow blogger. I've found myself shedding huge tears but enable to explain why to family members who have not been to the same places.

As I write this, I acknowledge that my biggest heartbreak was losing my local friend Moira who had had breast cancer. We had remained close but as ever with young children to raise, time to meet stretched away. We did speak regularly and one day at the dinner table where the whole family were present as well as a of my daughter who knew Moira, I spoke of her and said I must call her. Around half an hour later, my daughter and her friend came back in the room. They paused and then told me my friend was in hospital. It turned out they had discussed this (with very wise and compassionate 13-year-old heads) and decided initially not to tell me, so as not to upset me. However, when I mentioned calling, they decided to let me know. 'She has difficulty with her breathing', they said quietly. I had a cold clasp at my throat. I knew the likely cause and it seemed I was right: she had metastatic breast cancer. Cue at least six more years of chemotherapy; of short hair, longer curls and back to short again. The sickness of chemotherapy, the breathlessness of lung metastases, the pain of bone cancer and finally the brain symptoms that hastened the end. The harrowing cycle and diagnoses that emerged with each layer unfolded, gave her time with family that without treatment, she would not have had. Her children were a little older and more prepared than 11 years previously. But it was not easy, as anyone living through this knows. Moira faced it with humour, courage, and dignity. I saw her a mere two days before she died, we spoke, and she was still making jokes but also wanting to say her calm goodbyes. I'm weeping as I write this, 20 years later, and I still think I see her in crowds, until I remember. I took the announcement of her death with tears but calmly. The next day I was driving to work in Argyll, past Loch Lomond. I turned into a parking place and let the beauty of the spot help me let go of my grief, alone and held by the place and time.

I'm so sad she missed growing old. She would have been both wise and great fun. I've lost so many other friends since Moira. But none that affected me so much. The shared journey is part of it of course - but also the fact that, with her death, some of my protective bubble of denial ('it won't affect me', etc.) burst very painfully. My overwhelming fear was always not being there for my children. Her death made me face that one, at least until I could hide it away again.

The diagnosis of long-term conditions and serious illness has a destabilising effect on most families and friends. When this illness is life-limiting it maybe is the first-time people have faced death - and we tend to hide death away in our culture. Tragically, the pandemic has deepened that cavern between life and death. A last goodbye over Facetime is beyond contemplation. I've found the place I'm least fearful of cancer is in the Maggie's Centre. Its where most of us feel able to speak about cancer and about death. It's there I've spoken and written about fears and sat in that unspoken acknowledgement of them too.

Illness and disability have left me feeling demanding and selfish because I've needed so much support. And like most of us, I do like to be of help to others, whenever I can too. I feel more part of life when I'm able to help. Psychologists tell us we need three things in life to be happy or content; we need to love, to be loved, and to have a purpose. That doesn't change just because we are ill, disabled and / or dying. That purpose may be making soup for our grandchildren or looking after our pets or indeed sharing ourselves in the support of others. Peer support can be a boon for all involved. What a gift it can be, whether its formal or informal. I've experienced both and they've been life-changing.

■ Reflections for professionals

My friend and colleague, David Reilly, did some research in a primary care setting. He offered his WEL programme (Wellness Enhancement Learning - WEL)[15] to people with long-term conditions referred by their GP, to give them support and information to manage. At the beginning he shows the captured data on the list of conditions that the people referred are living with. The list was long and covered everything from

[15] www.theWEL.org

diabetes to depression. The programme was found to be extraordinarily successful, not just in changing things like diabetes outcomes but when participants followed up with the GPs they were asking new questions and in new language. The doctors were curious to learn more, especially as they saw things change for people. This resulted in a group of general practitioners and the wider team doing a WEL course themselves. What was interesting that the initial survey identified that they too had a long list of conditions, remarkably like those of their patients. They too were struggling with their health, and subject to the same cultural influences. The advance of long-term conditions and cancer is a population leveller. This realisation also triggered a community response to do more for community health. We all know it's not enough to prescribe pills, many of which have names that start with anti-, and it's hard to deal with the cognitive dissonance that dishing out advice that you don't heed yourself creates.

Workplace culture can normalise things like working through lunchbreaks and an increasing workload which is expected to be absorbed. This creates the mental health issues like depression, anxiety, and stress symptoms - similar again to those of their patients. So, this is not a case of peer-support vs professional support - it is recognising the opportunity in all of us being open to working and learning together. The reality is none of us have a guarantee of long-term health. All we can do is improve our wellbeing and accept the challenge that changes in health can bring.

As professionals, though, we are probably also likelier to live in the more affluent postcodes, where our neighbours don't have to use foodbanks or rely on universal credit. The pandemic has shone a harsh light on the reality of poverty in this supposedly rich country of ours. If you plot the incidence of Covid-19 and the highest death rates in the UK, then these correlate strongly with areas of deprivation and areas with high populations from ethnic minorities.[16][17] It's no coincidence the high-density populations of the West of Scotland, the ex-mining and shipbuilding communities of the North of England and Northern Ireland, the de-industrialised midlands of England, and the ex-mining

---

[16] Deaths due to COVID-19 by local area and deprivation - Office for National Statistics (ons.gov.uk)
[17] COVID-19: Health inequalities and recovery (local.gov.uk)

communities of Wales that have lost the most. Policies like universal basic income are maybe the best hope for less deaths in a future pandemic, rather than solely relying on increased health resources.

The increase in mental health issues during the pandemic has also helped us confirm the importance of human connection. Typically, third sector organisations at local or national level offer peer support approaches that are so needed, but are little known about. Knowing what's available or at least how to find it might be the best thing professionals can do to improve well-being. Developing a mutual respect where each supports the other in their role is not only crucial at community level, but at 1-1 partnership working as well. My sense is when we let go of being the expert and work as a fellow human being offering their own gifts on the journey back to health, it can be truly transformation for all involved.

Element Seven:

Learn how to process your new diagnosis

I'm curious to know if your first response to your new diagnosis is or was: *why, I'm fine?* We often reject the fact that the diagnosis has had an impact. When I was first diagnosed with asthma, it wasn't particularly stressful. My professional role meant I understood it, and I felt so much better after preventative treatment. But the first time I had a serious flare up, I was scared and disabled by it. That was the point I felt the impact and took it seriously. Even more challenging, I recognised a pattern: when I was overworking and over-tired, it would flare up again. To change things, I didn't just need to take medication (which I did dutifully), I needed to focus on self-care and on self-management of the condition itself. The difficult decision I finally had to take (following an earlier breast cancer occurrence) was to stop working full time, and avoid long travel days with the loneliness of a quietening airport or train as I awaited a last flight, or an empty train with no buffet car after Newcastle. I loved the job, but I could not sustain its pace without becoming ill. With both cancer and asthma to consider, I had to leave and grieve for my health and my job.

I believe finding mindfulness really improved both my health and the asthma as well. Learning to breathe to expand my lung capacity as well as to reduce the tension and anxiety I was holding in my body, has been so immensely powerful. Talking therapies have helped in the past, especially as a safe place for a cathartic release and letting go of old traumas.[18] But I knew in time there was something else I needed. With mindfulness I found the deeper listening to my body released what I was holding inside It's less a conscious knowing and more of an embodied process that mindfulness can locate with practice. Ours is a culture that prioritises intellectual knowledge which is vital for diagnoses, and treatments where they exist - but that's not enough to heal. To heal we do need to process and find acceptance in a way to live fully with our situation.

Accepting a diagnosis of diabetes has a significant impact on outcomes for people. Parents of children with Type 1 diabetes find their lives are transformed by it. For some it becomes almost an obsession and /or a point of conflict, especially in adolescence. Family dynamics can be significantly impacted on. Adolescents can be particularly vulnerable: using their insulin to lose weight, for example, can have a huge impact on their long-term health that is rarely understood (or is denied) by them. Diet can become a stress point as well, and it's easy for family and specialist teams to get caught up in judgements, rather than seeking to understand. It's so easy to get caught up in games that damage health and relationships.

The experienced diabetes specialists work with biochemical results and see the person beyond the condition and work through what matters to them. This protects families and professionals from creating dependencies and supports the person to process the reality of their condition, helping them to integrate it in their life. There are many apps supporting the biochemical management of diabetes, but people also need the psychosocial skills, including human connection and compassion. On average now, people with type 1 diabetes lose a decade of their lives and it will take more than new drugs or technology to fix that.

The approach of trauma-informed practice is now more available across mental health and A&E and ICUs, which is hugely welcome. A 'what's happened to you?' rather than a 'what's the matter with you?' approach may enable a more human-centred practice with long-term conditions too. The patient's experience of a significant diagnosis as a trauma is something that professionals may forget, as it's so familiar to them.

[18] The Body Keeps the Score, Besse Van Der Volk; 2014, Penguin books.

Trauma is also understood as playing a complex part of triggering long-term illness. The seminal study into ACE (adverse childhood events) by Kaiser Permanente[19] looked at the incidence of people with serious illness and long-term conditions, who also had a history of trauma. The mechanism is complex and not the focus of this book, however it's valuable to have information about what is a crucial part of an individual's story. Similarly, to PTSD, there are ways to support recovery from trauma with people who had told no one about their history until this point. It's been found that even the telling of the story supports ongoing wellbeing. The study showed that trauma affects physical as well as mental health. Serious illnesses like cancer and heart disease are more common in those who have experienced trauma even when smoking, drugs and alcohol behaviours are allowed for. There is a full circle of impact, which indicates the necessity for interventions that support the telling of story, as well as and approach involving deeper listening, non-judgement and compassion by practitioner or skilled peers. Without that, the processing of the condition may be impacted on. 'What has happened to you?' is a hugely an important part of the process, alongside 'what matters to you?'. These person-centred approaches offer a very different way of working, where the practitioner needs active listening as a core part of their offer.

The Kaiser Permanente research identified that a considerable number of children live with significant issues like poverty, neglect, abuse, and violence, and with drug and alcohol abuse and mental health issues in their parents. Research conducted into epigenetics[20] (Epigenetics is the study of how your behaviours and environment can cause changes that affect the way your genes work.) itself has shown these effects not only impact on the current generation but also those that follow. These effects are so significant yet may never have been spoken about. When trauma then is held in the body, rather than processed, it even changes the DNA. It is found that when people are given the opportunity to voice their experiences (and the more they do, the bigger the impact), this will enable a significant shift.

---

[19] The Relation Between Adverse Childhood Experiences and Adult Health: Turning Gold to Lead. VJ Felitti Ncbi.nim.nih.gov
[20] What is Epigenetics? | CDC

The rollout of mindfulness in some schools is a welcome intervention which will allow children to develop a language of compassion for themselves and others, and then build up resources in their lives. Using a breathing technique to calm the system begins to help them manage stress and relax. Teachers also notice changes in behaviour and these practices increase the childrens' capacity to learn. So, children can become more resilient and be open to a culture which itself is more open and transparent and above all, compassionate. Trauma informed education and care aims to break the cycle in childhood.

Trauma informed care is an important approach to enabling wellbeing but is yet to become mainstreamed. The treatment of post-traumatic stress disorder[21] is being informed by this approach as well. The first understanding of PTSD came from military service, from what was called shell shock in the first world war.

Studies have shown there is evidence that people following a stay in ICU are at risk of ongoing symptoms like PTSD. They have described nightmares, sleep disorders, anxiety, and pain. The drugs can also cause hallucinations that sit in that place between reality and nightmare. Reading of people's experience after surviving a time in ICU I felt a shiver up my broken spine. Even now as I write this my hands shake again, and my heart is racing. I had three ongoing hallucinations which tormented me with their reality and my lack of power to change things. One of them which involved a man returning to Bulgaria with his wife and dog, who would all face being shot if we didn't help. The dog was especially at risk of being killed. I was so anxious to help, that several days later, when I was in HCU and no longer ventilated, I asked my husband what had happened with them. He was bemused by and alarmed at my bizarre question. My attempted explanation made me run out of energy. I find it difficult to write about the others as it involves such fear and helplessness. I don't recall a reason for this but I also became very afraid of one of my named nurses and dreaded their shifts. Over two years on it still triggers me.

What we do know is that if people do not have support with these symptoms, they can develop longer term serious mental health issues. They can be treated, though, and ideally people will not be left to seek

---

[21] PTSD Common in ICU Survivors, Needham. www.hopkinsmedicine.org/news/media/releases/ptsd-common-in-icu-survivors

support from unhealthy coping mechanisms that numb their symptoms. Talking therapies can help, as can peer support. Medicine can help but may not be enough on its own. Yoga and meditation have been found to resolve symptoms of trauma as well. The focus in general needs to be on the integration of mind and body.

There are also variations of cognitive behaviour therapies that can help people let go of distorted beliefs, and associated self-talk, that risk reinforcing the effects of trauma - especially in situations where it is layered with experience of abuse.

In recent years EMDR (eye movement desensitisation and reprocessing)[22] has been found to be enormously valuable. The technique helps to access the trauma but enables it to be seen as in the past and part of a bigger picture for example. It's known to have had success where other techniques have not. This technique has become more known and available in the NHS.

With the impact of the pandemic not only affecting people who have had covid-19 but also healthcare staff, it's possible, even likely, that many will go undiagnosed. So how do you recognise the signs and symptoms of PTSD? Flashbacks, nightmares, repetitive images, or sensations, sweating, trembling and feeling sick are all potential symptoms. They may also involve depression, headaches, difficulty concentrating and excessive irritability and anger.

These can also be symptoms of other medical or social conditions, and what matters is that anyone with symptoms gets the support they need - and not simply medication. Also, it's important people feel able to speak up and ask for help. There is often support in third sector organisations and people do need to be able to find them so signposting from statutory services is crucial.

'Time heals' is so often repeated, but unresolved trauma won't simply go with time. It will sit in our bodies and thoughts. But with appropriate help it can get better.

---

[22] Treatment - Post-traumatic stress disorder - NHS (www.nhs.uk)

◼ Reflections for professionals

The role trauma plays in long-term health, both physical and mental, is a relatively recent discovery in mainstream health care. As professionals we would see the families with recurrent problems, and children who too often grew up to repeat patterns. But the mechanism of that, and more importantly how to break the cycle, other than with social change, remained out of reach. A different dialogue can now be opened, enabling conversations around what has happened to them. That dialogue can be therapeutic.

Secondary trauma may be something not yet fully understood or identified. The professionals working in ICU, A&E, social care, and children's services are susceptible to secondary trauma. It is crucial that managers are aware of this in the teams who are at most risk. Burnout is one manifestation, as are high levels of sick leave, depression, cynicism, anger, working constantly and being unable to switch off or delegate, tearfulness . . . you can probably add to the list . . .

So, people leave, retire early, go off on long-term sick, move to different parts of the service - and the loss of expertise to the care services consequently grows. Supervision in services like social work is designed to pick up issues and help to prevent them, but it's often the first appointment in the diary to go when people are stressed. And for the health professions, supervision is rarely available.

Could a trauma informed approach help? Could regular peer support, group supervision and appropriate referral for specialist services stop people leaving or carrying a burden of sickness that is very damaging to them? Those of us drawn to working in the caring professions need to be aware of people with a high number of (ACE's) Adverse Childhood Events,[23] not least because we ourselves have higher number of ACE's than the general population. It's beyond the work of this chapter to explore the causes of that, but it's important to be aware of our own potential triggers. This doesn't mean we shouldn't work where we might be triggered, rather that we become fully aware of the risk, and should this happen, we have somewhere to process it. The

---

[23] Adverse childhood experiences and chronic illness. (chronicillnesstraumastudies.com)

wounded healers are often deeply understanding and empathic, but we do need to process our own experiences so we can separate our needs from those of our clients/patients/carers.

When I started nursing, we were not encouraged to get too close to patients - as though we were somehow a different species, the specialists who knew all the answers. That lead to making it hard to ask for help where our own health was concerned. The pandemic has shone a more realistic light on this. We faced the virus together and carers, from health and social care, have died at higher rates than the general population. We are not immune to anything, after all, and certainly not to the pain we carry. From the photos of nurses' faces flared up by wearing PPE all the time, to care home workers seeing their clients lose the will to live when separated from families for months on end, to those who held their phones up for families to say their goodbyes - trying to weigh the impact from covid on staff feels both imperative and overwhelming.[24]

What is critical is that staff feel able to ask for help and see that as a strength rather than a weakness. It's often after the crisis that its true impact is felt. We are all affected in some way by the experience of the pandemic, so this is not about patients or care professionals, it's about all of us. We are involved in the complex dynamic of all our shared humanity, and it's that creative mix that produces the shared learning, kindness and compassion which gets the best outcomes for all. And helps us have hope for the future.

---

[24] NHS workers will need help to manage the trauma of the Pandemic. M Frankel. Feb 15 2021 www.theconversation.com

Element Eight:

Understanding grief and loss

Many diagnoses involve a loss that needs processed. Even when a diagnosis is initially welcome as it explains much, it has an impact our self-image at the very least. Loss is an integral part of a long-term condition which is rarely recognised in traditional forms of treatment. Too often, when people have completed the more acute or recognisable forms of treatment, they are seen as being fine now by family and friends. That's it over with, the scar has healed, the hair has grown, the lippy has gone on. Maybe, but for the person this may just be at the point at which the real sense of loss begins.

In cancer care some of these endings have rituals like ringing a bell, even in the face of those with secondary cancer who know that for them, that bell won't toll. When my radiotherapy finished, I had a good lunch with a friend, and a bottle of fizz that evening. But as the weekend stretched out, I realised just how much things had changed in my life, and it was only now that I had some time to process it. Andrew had recorded a concert by James Taylor, a rare event even then. I love his songs and his voice. He started to sing a song written by his good friend Carol King, 'You've got a friend' and the ties that had held me together let go. I cried and cried, we both did.

Years later I heard Carol King sing this song live in Hyde Park and it still had the same effect. Do those scars ever heal? Two weeks after my radiotherapy ended, my dad went into a hospice. I was struggling, not least because I was losing my much-loved father, and he was dying from cancer. My fears had to be faced, but I did know my situation was different, a point I made very clear to the children. The hospice doctor took some time with me one afternoon. I spoke to her about my fears, my dad had been told he had the disease early too. She said, 'but your dad has lived six years since then'. I was 38. I realised then that her idea of a good outcome and mine were scarily different.

I have found that when people ask, 'how are you?', I don't know where to start, so I just say 'I'm fine'. I minimise my own feelings as I want to protect the people around me - I know they too have struggled. I say little but that's when my blog has helped. My experience is that it is after writing it my mood dips and I finally begin to process my loss. And it's all so multi-layered: there is the loss of health, the loss of strength, the change to self-image, and the loss of the future you took for granted. Cancer in young people can also mean the loss of the ability to have a child, a devastating outcome for many. The harvesting of embryos can change that outcome but still not without complexity.

It's true for so many long-term conditions that there is a loss of what you planned and what you thought life would be like. I know I'm not alone in doing some bargaining with God, even when I'm not sure I believe in God. And every deal involved to being there for my children. 'Let me see them through school...' and studies, graduations, travels, weddings and every milestone I never wanted to miss. I never assumed I would be lucky enough to be a Grannie. So, when I've got into my 40s, 50s, then 60s I've been delighted to still be here. However bruised, battered, disabled, disfigured and grey I've become, I've remained grateful for every year.

The grief cycle as described by Kubler-Ross will be familiar to many. We have a culture of mastery in Western Society so we see the nice, neat process and think its ok, I can do that. I can do that and miss the painful, messy part. But then we realise it's not a simple process of loss and it's not a neat circle at all. What's often forgotten is that Kubler Ross was studying the dying and their process differs, especially in that there is an end. And they too often don't follow a neat pattern. People can resist death, to an extent that puts at risk the relative's ability to cope. Some people will cling on to ensure they are there for a special date, a son back from Australia or a new child in the family. Death, dying, and grief are complex processes, and do not unfold in a linear, time predictable way. The experience of different components will vary from person to person.

The Stages of grief as described in the NHS information are the following:

o   Accepting your loss is real

o   Experiencing the pain of grief

o   Adjusting your life without the person (or loss of role, pet, health)

o   Putting less emotional energy into grieving and putting it instead into something new

These can take a few months or years and the emotions attached to them can be much more painful and messy than words can convey. Feelings of shock or numbness can last a while as the reality sets in. During lockdown, the separation from family members will have had a complicating effect on the acceptance of loss for some. That's something to be aware of: loss itself has been locked down.

It's so important to tune in to your needs. To be kind to yourself. The waves of sadness and crying are overwhelming and exhausting. That can be an important factor when trying to return to work; the fatigue can be disabling. And it's an indication that physically and mentally you are not recovered.

Our emotions can be complicated, particularly if the relationship wasn't straightforward. Or if the loved one knowingly didn't take care of their health. Anger is often present ('why me?', 'how could you leave me?' and so on). Guilt too can be a devastating emotion - all the 'shoulds' can haunt us: 'I should have phoned earlier, I shouldn't have left, I should have been a better partner, I shouldn't have smoked' . . .

Many of us can have regrets after loss, but many too will have the balancing effect of happier memories. The routines and rituals of funerals and wakes, and the many other processes and rituals of different cultures and religions, are a valuable part of letting go. Again, Covid has affected these gatherings, where we tell our stories, pray, sing/chant, and begin the process of letting go.

I dare say I'm not alone in being haunted by the thought of so many dying in hospital or a care home with a stranger. That separation, when both parties need to feel the love of the other, is so sad and painful. The chance to say you love them to put to rest some words or deeds that hurt in the past, to hug, to hold hands, is lost. It is important to have some ritual, commemoration, or symbolic act to make space to experience the loss, the pain, the grief and to celebrate the good. This is merely part of a process, not 'closure'. *Closure* is a word from American English that can suggest there is a date after which we can go, 'ok that's done now'. Now we are beginning to question if that is just a myth. Certainly, for most of us, grief shifts and changes and lessens over time. But a trigger can take you straight back and the pain be as acute as day one.

I experienced this recently. When the neurosurgeon told me that the growth attached to my spinal cord was going to leave me paralysed from my lower back down, and that I would likely lose control of my bladder and bowel, I experienced a rush of fear and shock that took my breath away. Over time since the surgery, I have adapted to walking with support at home, and to using a wheelchair or mobility scooter outside. My bladder and bowel control seems to have been saved by the surgery. I have kept busy, and lockdown has helped in some ways as I can do my work without travelling. A zoom call normalises us wheelchair users. I have used writing too as a creative outlet. I was asked in a class about a favourite trip and without a second thought, I started to write about a beach down the coast from Edinburgh. As the poem emerged, I realised with an overwhelming sense of loss, that I couldn't get back there because of the inaccessibility of the route to it. I wanted to howl but of course I suppressed it on a zoom call! I made the point in the last verse, but I dared not speak of my grief for fear of falling apart. That is still with me as I write. At times I feel a tide of loss threaten to overwhelm me. I hold it back, even when I know I should trust myself to find a way to sail with it. If someone tried to speak to me about closure it would trigger anger, I'm sure. Like I'm not supposed to keep feeling this. I suspect for now I can't let go because that way I must accept its reality.

My Mother died of Alzheimer's the March before my mobility really began to decline. She was taken by a chest infection linked to a virus that was too much for her frail body. But it gave us some weeks with her to show her our love. Dementia and specifically Alzheimer's has been described as having many losses. There are several stages, but for me they don't necessarily connect to the stages of grief.

Yes, those initial stages shocked, so much that they could be measured on the emotional Richter scale. Many of us will deny this kind of shock to others and, even more so, to ourselves. I experience so many losses once I realised that Mum was hanging on to her control of her life by her fingernails as it slid away from her. Her tablets in small clusters of hope she will take the right ones. The missed appointments, blamed on the post or a friend's mistake. Poor retention of information and the need to retell good, or bad, news. A gradual realisation that she could no longer live at home. We too were feeling the pain of her loss and the shame she carried around because of her decline. Then the shock at accepting the imminent final illness because we realised what that would mean. The family got a few weeks to say their goodbyes and show their love in all the ways they could. And then after all that she was gone. On a cold March Day, she slipped away. This for me is the kind of loss that carves away at you, jagged edges and holes that can't be filled. But for most of us, we go on, the pain of these years slowly eases, and the recognition that you still feel orphaned, even at the tender age of 61, leaves you a wee bit wiser and mindful of others when they meet that place too.

Our own experience of grief does affect how we deal with others that follow. You know too that how they feel at first changes and that emotional and that physical shock will ease. But if, on the other hand, someone experienced a significant prior loss, especially in childhood, and not been able to process it - perhaps it wasn't faced up to in the family - then another grief may trigger a much bigger reaction, and sometimes lead to a mental health issue.

Similarly, facing loss of health, including having a mastectomy or learning to live with a stoma, takes time and is an individual path. My best message is to say don't do it alone, link to people who will lift you up, take help and don't rush, it will take its own time. Don't get stuck with the 'shoulds' or collude with hiding away the painful 'unsaids'. You may need to speak about the person who has gone, when others want to do the opposite. It is their right to stay silent, as it is yours to talk. Just find the right people to be around and when they offer help, let them, and guide them as to what they can help with. And there are times when it feels like too much, I know, and it's ok to say that.

My Dad died of cancer two weeks after I finished radiotherapy to my breast. I was used up, trying to protect my children and my family. We know the power of the word cancer. Dad died in a short timescale, really, when I was trying to hold my family and to convince them that my cancer was different from Grandad's. Each loss worsened the other. It was his love that had often kept me putting one foot in front of the other. He really understood what was happening to me, and so I wanted to scream, 'don't leave me now, of all times. I was working as a practice nurse and doing my best swan impression that fooled no one. One of the older, kind, and experienced GPs, when asking after me, said something I've never forgotten. As I mentioned earlier in the book he said, 'there will be better times again'. I experienced it as a warm blanket of hope. And he was right.

■ Reflections for professionals

To work successfully with others on grief, we need to be willing to face our own. If you find yourself avoiding this area or that you find it difficult to address, then it's probably helpful to you to talk to someone about it. We carry lots of shoulds which can be real burdens, and exhausting. We are humans with all our flaws and aspirations as well as shared experiences.

COVID-19 has in so many ways highlighted our shared experiences. Not only are we in it together but those of you working at the so-called front line are at greater risk from the extra exposure, and if you are from a BIPOC (black and persons of colour group) you are at an even higher risk. The collective grief around COVID-19 is a huge burden that NHS and care teams are carrying. There is and probably will be a large unmet need. Not all this needs to be medicalised. Maybe a support group can help release feelings and learn from others that we aren't alone. You will need good listeners around you. There may be local charities who have developed services to support people with things like artforms, including music, painting, writing, singing. All could help process and release feelings. These feelings need an outlet, or they stay. If we feel overwhelmed or our mood is low or have other symptoms it's important to speak to a doctor. PTSD is treatable, don't struggle without help.

■ Stages of grief

Professionals will be aware of these stages and the circle often used to describe them but also will know the messiness that applies in real life. Those stages and symptoms may not however be recognised in people living with long-term conditions. Their loss may be expressed differently. What we can experience as their resistance or denial is related to their grief and inability yet to accept the new reality. There's also often fear as they recall how the same condition affected others in their family. Talking through that fear, acknowledging it, can help someone see that they are different, and the fear is something they've created from a difficult experience. Even within my lifetime, treatments have radically changed, enabling people to better manage their condition. Their fears may be unnecessary in the current situation.

In this situation the best thing you can do is listen. Ask open questions and really listen to the reply. When someone is struggling with loss, we need not offer tidy solutions, just need to listen without judgement and show we have really heard. COVID-19 has really changed some of the dialogue around serious illness and long-term conditions. It has already been recognised as a condition that can affect all parts of the body and leave people with what's become known as Long Covid. Fatigue is a common symptom; others vary but can affect the respiratory, cardiac, and neurological systems. So far, many trials are being conducted but a cure for or effective treatments of symptoms remain unknown, apart from the need for focussed self-care.[25] [26] Many people with Long Covid were completely healthy before, so their experience of loss is visceral. Those who have experienced CFS (chronic fatigue syndrome), ME (myalgic encephalitis) and Fibromyalgia will recognise some similar

[25] Long covid-mechanisms, risk factors, and management. www.bmj.com BMJ 2021;374: n1648
[26] theBMJ https://bit.ly/BMJlong

symptoms, in particular fatigue and brain fog. Many of them struggled to get a diagnosis and for that diagnosis to be respected and taken seriously. I sincerely hope that will not be the experience of those with long COVID-19.

Fortunately, however, COVID-19 has opened the door to talk about grief and loss. As professionals it may feel overwhelming to cope with it on such a scale. Understandably, you might feel it's not your role, but hopefully this chapter amongst other studies, helps you recognise that in many ways it's not that complex: it's about deep listening, human compassion, and kindness.

Element Nine:

Nature, Nurture and Food

In-spite of being called a National Health Service, what it really does, often extremely well, is it treats illness. But if you are looking to be healthy, it is rarely the setting for discussions on matters like healthy eating, or source of good information at the time of acute illness. There is no doubt that in recent years that awareness has improved, but too often there are mixed messages around treating illness and wellbeing.

Many agencies provide information on eating well but at the same time we are witnessing the rise of foodbanks and malnutrition because of hunger due to poverty and the cost of healthy food. Food poverty - and hunger - are a huge issue in our society. During the pandemic the delivery of food parcels to those in need became a daily reality. And that need has deepened with the cost-of-living crisis of 2022/3.

I'm so aware when writing this that food to survive can be very different from food to thrive. The impact of the global food industry has produced food full of hidden additives, salt and of course sugar. It also made it more difficult to make healthy choices when we are bombarded with colourful, fun packaging and food that we are told tastes fun as well. Sugar-based foods activate the opiate receptors in our brain and through the 'reward centre' this leads to compulsive consumption. This behaviour is difficult to avoid. My generation, the baby boomers, emerged from rationing into the availability of all kinds of food in new shops called supermarkets. It was heady stuff. And add to that, in the culture I grew up in, like many others, giving food equates to giving love. So, we make cakes, sweets and Grannies are often the suppliers of so called goodies like biscuits and chocolate. My Gran used to give us a crunchie each week when she visited. It tasted so good.

In the last 20-30 years, people have been nagged to eat better and still we've got fatter as a nation. The growth of cooking and baking programmes on our TVs has been exponential and yet sits in contrast to the amount of takeaway food we eat. It's a paradox that fascinates me. Perhaps it's that food has become functional in our world - we eat on the go, fast as possible with little pleasure - so we need to find the pleasure in food elsewhere?

I find dieting impossible. I've always been heavier than I wanted to be, since my thirties and especially since having breast cancer. But can I diet? No, it makes me focus on food and nothing else matters, so I eat more . . .

I did the WEL course (wellness enhancement learning) after struggling with my wellbeing following a cancer diagnosis. I was tired and low at that point. The course was developed by my friend and colleague Dr David Reilly after working for many years with people who had struggled with their health and were living with cancer and long-term conditions like diabetes or ME. Day Two of the Five-day WEL is about food. If I'm honest my ears pricked up, but my heart sank. Another session being nagged at, was my assumption, but I'm always drawn to understand more about food, and here we really did. No nagging, just information and an invitation. I suggest you have a look to see what he says on the WEL website,[27] it's very inspiring and revealing. Essentially, he suggests that we eat food. So far so good. By that he means food that's as close to having been in the ground as possible. Move away from processed food and extend your vegetable consumption and eat a wide a range of colours: eat the rainbow, as new colours mean new vitamins and minerals. Eat as much organic food and fermented food as you can. This ensures the flora in the gut can support your immune system too. Frozen food is better than canned as freezing preserves the

---

[27] Epigenetics is the study of how your behaviours and environment can cause changes that affect the way your genes work.

nutrients. More recently I've been aware of the work of ZOE[28] that gained prominence during the pandemic, raising awareness of the importance of nutrition and health.

As I listened and processed the new information from the WEL it occurred to me that its message was simple, and this made sense. Consider, too, the industrialisation of animals as food products. This has a devastating impact on the animals, who are often kept inside, given hormones and antibiotics. These unfortunate, unhealthy animals live in the dark with no sunshine - of course this impacts on us.

I have found this approach to healthy eating to be very helpful. The focus is not on deficit like calorie reduction, it's on wellbeing - and to recover or live well with a condition, you need to eat healthy food. But there are circumstances when that just isn't enough. There are now consistent findings that many of us in the Northern Hemisphere are deficient in Vitamin D3. Largely it's because we go outside less, and we get less sunshine. During the pandemic those shielding were offered Vit D as they were not going out. If you are deficient in Vitamin D the recommended dose is to take a supplement of Vit D3 of 10 microgrammes daily. Some studies have looked at whether vitamin D could help treat people with Covid 19, but they aren't conclusive. It's thought that Vitamin D may help with the inflammatory process and that it supports the immune system. As part of your diet, it's good to have oily fish, red meat, eggs, and liver regularly. If you are vegan, seek a range of organic vegetables, avoid processed food and take supplements. The ZOE team use data-driven research to tackle global health issues. The ongoing PREDICT[29] studies are the world's largest in-depth nutritional research. They have a particular interest in gut microbe health and dietary inflammatory processes. This affirms the work by Dr Reilly and confirms that nutrition is a much more complex issue than early dietary advice allowed. To support health while living with long-term conditions, it's important to arm ourselves with this kind of knowledge and for NHS advisers to be up to date in the advice they give.

---

[28] ZOE—Understand how food affects your body (joinzoe.com)
[29] https://joinzoe.com/whitepapers/the-predict-program

Obesity[30] is the most talked about dietary issue and its impact on health is well documented. The dieting industry is also enormous. Yet one thing we do know about dieting is that it doesn't work in the long-term. The benefits largely disappear in a year. But it serves a huge industry to tell us that it does imply that we can only be happy if we are slim. Bring in some Instagram influencers and stir the pot and we find a growing incidence of eating disorders. The Royal College of Psychiatrists[31] state that around 15% of young women and 5.5% of young men have an eating disorder, often a mixture of the different types. The causes are of course multi-layered, with biological, social and psychological influences, including history of trauma, all likely to play a part.

So, it is true our relationship with food is complex. Obesity in the developed world is so common at a societal level, yet our solutions to date have largely been sought at individual level. And given that obesity is often tied up with so many social and psychological factors, including self-worth, it's curious that we think telling someone to lose weight will have the outcome we desire. Covid-19 has a greater impact on those who are overweight and obese. The effect of obesity on our health – as a contributory factor to diabetes, heart disease, cancer and more - is well known, and yet many who are obese are reluctant to go to visit health professionals. A common reason is that often their weight triggers shame, low self-esteem, depression, and suicidal thoughts. The obesity becomes a barrier to getting advice or treatment for other conditions. And obese individuals can be less successful in the workplace too. It's been said that obesity may be one of the few remaining socially acceptable prejudices. The WHO has confirmed that weight stigma is ubiquitous.

This is such a paradox: there has perhaps never been such focus on being the perfect shape, whilst also on the rising rates of obesity. The work of Brene Brown[32] on vulnerability and shame seeks to turn the focus on its head. Her research has found that what we need to start with is 'I am enough'. This statement is most likely to lead to change and help people improve their health and wellbeing.

[30] https://www.who.int. Obesity and health consequences.
[31] Position Statement on early intervention for eating disorders. Royal College of Psychiatrists PS03/19
[32] https://youtu.be/psN1DORYYV0 Brene Brown Listening to Shame.

Her suggestion is that what she calls 'wholehearted living' is the best route to wellbeing. This asks us to

▷ Let our whole selves be seen.

▷ To love with our whole hearts.

▷ To practice gratitude and joy.

▷ To start with I am enough.

The journey looking at food and nurture has taken us all the way from dieting, to eating, and believing in ourselves, recognising that we are enough.

■ Reflections for professionals

As with previous Elements, all these issues are also concerns for the professionals too. Obesity in the health and social care workforce has caused concern. This is often addressed by provision of access to healthier foods, but that has not resulted in change, because the internal and societal issues have not been addressed. Issues like trauma, yo-yo dieting, and self-esteem remain unexplored at individual and societal level.

Most health and social care professionals are affected by both primary and secondary traumas. Paramedics, as first responders, can be left with unexplored emotions, and recurrent stressful dreams. Care givers can be impacted with the death of a resident who has been their friend for many years. ICU and A&E staff bombarded with acute situations; community nurses support families through death and dying. All this part of their role, and comfort can be taken from doing a good job. But the times where something goes wrong can stay with you forever. And workers in all those roles and many others have seen trauma on a massive scale since the start of the pandemic. It's hard to even compute unless you've been there yourself and know that you've just had to keep going; perhaps knowing you will go into your shift the next day and find all the people you were caring for have died.

It's thought a significant part of the workforce is experiencing a form of PTSD. If there is no outlet for the discussion of these extreme experiences and safe ways to decrease stress cannot be found, then what can happen is *numbing*. That can result in using food, alcohol or drugs to provide some relief and numb the impact of chronic stress. Good team cohesion and support may well ameliorate the stress but where that doesn't happen or isn't fostered then the risk of numbing remains.

The pandemic is likely to be having a huge impact on wellbeing. Having support to explore the experience with your peers could make a significant difference. Facilitated peer groups could be helpful, as well as yoga, and meditation, as has been explored earlier. What's most important is that the need is met as well, and safely, as possible.

The message around Vitamin D is also hugely important for all staff working with the public. There are many resources about where and how to eat the healthiest food so I will not explore that further here, but reiterate that tackling obesity must be a holistic, person-centred process. Helping people understand how to access healthy food and how to avoid processed food can help. But food is political too. Do people have the money for food? Food poverty is common in the UK and foodbanks by their nature find it hard to offer fresh food, where the best nutrition lies.

Even where there is sufficient money the pressure to buy high sugar-content processed food, or high-fat processed food is immense and Just Eat, Uber Eat will deliver it straight to your door. Our lifestyles make this hard to avoid. Only legislation is likely to change this longer term.

Trauma informed care will hopefully become a mainstay of supporting people with obesity in the future. Moving away from judgement and potential for shaming, we will be asking questions like: *what matters to you? What happened to you? How best can I help you? What would a good outcome be for you?* And remembering the Brene Brown mantra, I am enough. Even as I write that, I have to remind myself of that too.

Element Ten: Self-Compassion

Throughout this book there is a theme of self-compassion. How can we find a place of wellbeing if we are not compassionate to ourselves? As you know I have grown up in Scotland, a fine place - however I notice that when I speak of self-compassion, I can sense toes curling in shoes. We're not ones to talk of love, especially in connection to ourselves. Our national Bard, Robert Burns, may have written of love in many ways but we're more likely to crack a joke when things get deeper, in these times.

As women, especially older women, we were brought up seeing our mothers ensure the men were fed first, and in tougher times women would go hungry to feed the rest of the family. Our more feminist generation continued to internalise beliefs such as they should attend to everyone bar themselves. Add in religion or austerity, and these beliefs are reinforced. Who, having seen it, can forget the scene in the film *I Daniel Blake*,[33] when the young mother grabbed a can of beans and hid behind the shelves, stuffing it in her mouth, driven by hunger, poverty, and self-neglect?

Gender has always been an issue in terms of how I see myself. I'm small and now because of a growth on my spine, I'm a wheelchair user. I'm easy to ignore and be one of the unseen. When I have had male CEOs. I have tended to confer superiority on them. I have had to manage myself, when I have been in a place of influence, not to defer - but when the time was right to state my beliefs and remember that 'I am enough.'

[33] https://www.bbc.co.uk/bbcfilm/films/i-daniel-blake

I have learned to do that in leadership roles. I now have much more self-esteem and I am more self-compassionate, but I've often learned from a hard experience.

We do need to acknowledge gender issues – including being aware of the pressures on men. Men in western society had been not encouraged to show their feelings. The phrase 'man up' says much about attitudes to expressing feelings. Someone trying to improve their mental health, or to process loss and grief, will not be helped by this type of attitude. Men are expected to be hard workers, good earners for their families, to be good dads as well as attentive husbands and friends. It's a tough juggling act, too, especially with young children wakening at night. If the only reaction to this is 'you are fortunate' or 'man up', it's no wonder that men are at increased risk of taking their own lives, particularly in their middle years.[34] Men are three times more likely to die by suicide than women and although rates have lowered in younger men, they have now increased in men aged 40-50. It's complex and certainly linked to austerity and deprivation.

So, exploring self-compassion sits in a context where there is a huge pressure on all of us, not least the Covid -19 pandemic, which has affected us so much and worsened loneliness and social isolation. For too many the reality is a reduced income and reliance on foodbanks and charities to feed themselves. It may seem trite to talk about compassion in the face of this, but it makes self-compassion, self-forgiveness, and self-care more crucial. In a world so influenced by marketing, maybe you see self-compassion as treating yourself - but what it really is, is what you notice in your self-talk. Instead of thinking: *I should be better at this, I'm not good enough, I'm a failure,* try saying: *I am worthy of love and respect, I am good enough at being a mum, I'm more than what I do – its who I am that counts.* As I wrote good enough at being a mum, a cloud lifted from me. Right now, I needed that reminder: it's always work in progress, but that is ok.

The good news about self-compassion is that we can learn, and we can improve. And that's the same whoever we are and whatever our situation. As I have said before, the most powerful learning I found at the start of my mindfulness journey was to realise that *you are not your*

---

34 Data introduction - ScotPHO

thoughts. Wow! I was stunned. What a gift that was. So, all those thoughts like *I'm not good enough* are just constructs shaped by my own story and experience. I had grown up being hard on myself, and maybe this is part of what has driven me to do all I have - but I've paid a high price for it. Years ago, as I was recovering from breast cancer treatment, I was working and studying as well as being a mother to young children. I started to notice that to keep everything going, I was ignoring all my needs. I was trying to meet the needs of children, my husband, my newly widowed mum, my dog and cat, my patients and colleagues, my studies - and not looking at myself. I've already mentioned the day I was driving towards Loch Lomond when I considered driving off the road. It was a strong compulsion that seemed to last a while. Fortunately, I realised then that I needed help, and my therapist helped me to see how little care I was showing myself. I needed some time off work to stop and reflect on how to change my behaviour. It wasn't easy but I was shocked by how in that moment I just wanted it all to stop. I didn't want to die; I just couldn't keep going.

This experience really taught me about the absolute necessity of self-compassion. We really need to bring awareness to the thoughts that drive us and know that we can change them to more compassionate and healing ones. This is an ongoing challenge for me, to ensure I'm giving priority to meeting my needs. Now I get warnings from pain if I physically stretch myself too much. It's also noticeable how my mind and body synchronise to help me recognise risk and I know now what to do. I notice the signs and think about *what am I learning here?* It's a lifelong learning for me as well as lifelong practice. Practising and fostering gratitude too is something that I find very grounding and balancing. Try this:

Test how self-compassionate you are | Kristin Neff (self-compassion.org)[35]

You may find it helpful at this stage to complete this 'compassion scale'. It's useful as a guide to your starting position and can help you understand more fully what is meant by self-compassion. Some of the answers may surprise you, and you might discover you are harder on yourself in certain circumstances. That's a great awareness to have as a

---

[35] Test how self-compassionate you are | Kristin Neff (self-compassion.org)

starting point – alongside remembering that self-compassion improves with some practice.

There are many ways to support your own self-compassion needs, and hopefully the book has already helped to identify some, such as challenging someone else's agenda and learned behaviours around that. Awareness is a large part of the process of change. Notice when you say should and think "what is that about for me", "what is it linked to?" You could try out the following '5 whys' technique around a 'should.' For example: *I should never get a poor result. Why? I don't like to fail at things. Why? I want my family to be proud of me. Why? Because they will only be proud of me if I do well.* Etc. Once you get to the 5th why or before that if it's very clear, check: *is this true?* So you are essentially quite quickly getting to the core of the issue. The awareness helps you stop and make a choice about how you respond. A bigger issue might require talking over with someone, to explore how to reframe it - which can be hard after years of holding a certain belief, but it can be done.

We've mentioned meditation already, and it's a very valuable approach for self-compassion. A core component of self-compassion is the loving kindness mindfulness meditation,[36] based on the Metta meditation in the Buddhist tradition. This meditation is best explained through actual meditation practice, and all the mindfulness apps will have a variation on it. Many people will find this difficult at the start, so please don't worry if you do too. It takes time to build up practice, and the impact grows with that. Be curious about where you get stuck, where the difficulties staying with the practice are. There is no wrong way to practice and there are longer and shorter meditations, from 5-25 minutes, all of which will give benefit.

There are now many apps which offer guided meditations, and you can use them to support your practice. It's best to look around to find a teacher you can most relate to. Kirsten Neff and Paul Gilbert have both written widely on self-compassion and the compassionate mind if you want to understand this more deeply. I hesitate to recommend more teachers as there are so many. An app like the Insight Timer offers access to many of them. Other apps include Headspace, Calm, The

---

[36] https://youtu.be/9cxtdiXBQDk

Mindfulness App, the Breathing App (can help to get the breathing right to begin with).

Self-care comes in many forms, including eating well, walking, swimming, dancing. The more we are in tune with our body's needs, the more compassionate we are being. In essence self-care is about building awareness of your thoughts and feelings and body sensations. Any activity that will contribute to awareness will increase your self-compassion in its wider sense. For example, the 'body scan' mindfulness meditation helps build awareness of the body, paying attention to each area of discomfort or ease, as part of the process of learning how mind and body influence each other.

For example, the Metta or Loving Kindness practice.

> Loving kindness practice:
>
> This is to show you the principle of the approach and to enable you to practice with some knowledge from a suitable app for you.
>
> First, we will settle into a meditation position that works for you; sitting, lying down, whatever seems right. Lying down you may want to put a blanket over you, sitting ensure your back is supported and feet supported by the ground. Either close your eyes or focus on something on the floor. And now look to your breath, taking about three breaths into the count of four and out to the count of six.
>
> The mantra within this meditation is: *May I be happy, may I be well, may I be safe, may I live with ease.* So next I invite you to say or think these words quietly to yourself, giving yourself time to engage with the words and reflect on them before you move on. Then recall someone you love; this can be a friend, a child or partner, a pet or a mentor or carer. So, then I invite you to say the words; *may you be happy, may you be well, may you be safe, may you live with ease.* Again, take your time, come back to your

breathing and settle, once you are ready, come back from the meditation and reflect on how that worked. This is a short version and may be a good one to start or end the day. It also may help you get used to the meditation approach and once you are confident with that you can move on to the next stage.

To continue with the loving kindness meditation, the next step is to recall someone you feel neutral about-someone you notice who serves you in a shop or delivers your mail. And to say to them *may you be happy, may you be well, may you be safe, may you live with ease*, engaging with the thoughts as you slowly repeat the phrases.

The next step is to think of someone you have a difficulty with who is currently in your life in some way and yes again you will say these words, engaging with the meaning and message; *may you be happy, may you be well, may you be safe, may you live with ease*. It's interesting to reflect on your feelings towards this person having gone through the process and to understand that yes, like you, they want to be happy, they also want to be well and to live with ease.

And the final stage is I invite you to picture the whole world, this troubled world, and to wish everyone; *may you be happy, may you be well, may you be safe, may you live with ease*. After this take some deeper breaths again and sit for a while reflecting on how you are now, what felt easy, what was difficult, how did you experience this in your body, where did your thoughts go, could you stay with the process and so on. This is a powerful meditation and a good platform for self-compassion. The more you practice this the more the process deepens and the greater the benefit.

Sleep is often an issue with diagnoses both of acute illness and long-term conditions, so a key part of self-care is good sleep hygiene. During the pandemic in 2020/21 sleep disorder was a significant problem. Existential angst affected so many of us. The collective anxiety was reinforced by constant news and rising numbers of deaths and the seriously ill. Couple that with being constantly locked down, and it was something akin to punishment, especially for those with no garden and children at home. The lack of routine added to that most definitely affected sleep. Busy brains, worry and lack of people or practices to help release tension all made things worse. Domestic tensions and abuse are frequently accompanied by a lack of sleep. There are so many causes of the usual sleep habits being disrupted. It is often a perfect storm affecting a key part of well-being, our sleep.

I recognise this reaction. When I was diagnosed with cancer or the spinal growth, sleep always has been the first casualty. Perhaps I could get to sleep alright but then I'd wake around 3am and start to fret. *What if . . .* is a particular favourite. How long . . .is another. *Will I be able to . . .* Fill in the blanks depending on the issue. I have been known to get up and consult Dr Google. (That never ended well: please don't do this, screen time disrupts sleep, it rarely helps and may be very unreliable, depending on the source.). Even with breast cancer, a subject I know well, I could still find something that made my heart race in a bad way. When I looked up the spinal issue it was grim but there was little actual information anywhere as its quite rare. NHS Information is generally best as it tempers information with compassion.

Wakening in the night, I've taken notes to stop my mind turning over thoughts. I've rehearsed speeches that I've never delivered and gradually I have adapted, grieved, and shed tears till I can't even cry any more. Talking about it mostly helps, but sometimes even that is too hard at first. I do know that for me I need to not fret about sleeplessness but accept this is normal and that it settles in time. There are some things that can help, should your sleep remain an issue.

First, keep a sleep schedule so you know what the pattern is. Then:

▷ Create a relaxing bedtime ritual.

▷ Avoid daytime naps (or keep them short)

▷ Exercise daily, appropriate to your situation

▷ Check your room temperature and light disruption (black out blinds can help)

▷ Deliberately wind down: shut off electrical devices like games and screens from laptops or phones.

▷ Try to adjust to circadian rhythms: reduce light in evenings and increase in mornings in the summer and vice versa in the winter.

▷ Avoid heavy meals, alcohol, nicotine, and caffeine in the evening.

▷ If you can afford to, check the comfort of pillows and mattresses, and change what you need to

▷ Do a mindful meditation before sleep or if you are lying awake.

▷ If you are tossing and turning, try reading or listening to audiobook or podcasts or have a warm drink.

▷ And finally, if problems continue do speak to your GP as they can also point to other issues.

The awareness we build will also affect how we relate to the world. Viktor Frankyl was a survivor of Auschwitz as well as other Nazi concentration camps. He was a young psychiatrist and neurologist when he was imprisoned. After the war he wrote a book called *Man's Search for Meaning* and developed the theory of logotherapy, which was quite unique in its thinking at the time. It was based on some fundamental beliefs, for example that each person at core is healthy. His approach is to help people identify their inner resources, and the tools to access that inner core. Logotherapy was based on Frankyl's early work and on his reflections about what had helped him survive the holocaust. The premise of his work is that humans are driven to find meaning and purpose in life. Frankyl believed that life's meaning could be determined by:

- ▷ Creating a piece of work or accomplishing a task

- ▷ By loving someone or experiencing something fully

- ▷ By accepting that difficult times are inevitable but that you can choose how you react

He also believed that poor mental health was related to an existential angst and if people could recognise that, and find meaning or purpose, then they could become and remain well. This is a very small part of a wide-ranging book, and I recommend reading it so you can take your own meaning from it.

Reflecting on this in the context of a pandemic, it does help me to understand the awful impact of the lockdown and the omnipresent fear of the virus and its potential impact on those we love. There can also be a sense of meaninglessness surrounding the loss of life and a powerlessness to change that. But there is also hope in his work, that a sense of purpose during this time will make a difference. It can be as simple as being focussed on keeping your family well, of looking after a pet, shopping for a neighbour, supporting teammates through tough times. The list is endless and it doesn't need to involve helping everyone, it's just about making a difference for someone.

Frankyl did find that even in the darkest of places and times, he witnessed compassion and kindness and that also helped the ability to keep going. The practice of gratitude sits alongside this. It is not a Pollyanna enforced smile, it's a practice that comes from the deepest acknowledgement of what enriches our lives and our genuine noticing of what brings life joy. Practising gratitude should not be done without compassion for others. This may sound smug but really, it's about knowing what you are deeply grateful for, whatever else is happening.

When people are faced with life changing diagnoses it can be hard to think of what to be grateful for every day. But it could just be noticing a spring flower opening, or a snowflake falling, and being caught by their unique beauty, a smile from a passer bye, a text from a friend. When we locate our gratitude we locate our own place in the world, grounded and more peaceful. If we can practise this regularly, then our brain recognises the change and starts to lay down new neural pathways. It becomes something we can do with ease. What a gift to self-compassion.

Many people find it helpful to keep a gratitude diary, to capture what they are grateful for at the start or end of the day. This can be especially helpful when we are struggling. It just shifts the perspective and the heart! If you try this practice, you will find it needs to be genuine - not what you think you should maybe write, but what you truly notice. It's a meditation that helps you lift your head and see the world freshly each time. But if you start with 'at least' there is a difference in the tone - like when someone says to you, for example, 'at least it happened through lockdown when you couldn't go anywhere anyway'. That tends to diminish the reality of the person's experience. The social isolation caused by the pandemic is so much worse if you are ill or are in pain. I've had so many 'at leasts' over the years: 'at least it's not cancer' - when it's a benign growth attached to my spine making me unable to walk and making me live with neurological pain. 'At least it's the good cancer', about breast cancer. 'At least you don't have to walk the dog' reduced me to tears, as that's the one thing I really wanted to be able to do. And I'm not perfect with this, I say it at times often about myself. The worst 'at least' is when you are denying your own pain and distress. [I recognise I do this to shut down conversations.]

For example, today I'm most grateful for a visit to the Royal Botanic Gardens in Edinburgh with friends. It's spring and the gardens are bursting with buds and colour. There is a cacophony of bird song. It's glorious. What are you grateful for today?

Self-compassion can be wrongly seen as the 'soft stuff', about being nice, doing things the easy way. But honestly, it's the tough stuff. To have compassion for yourself is also about being true to yourself, speaking up for your needs to be met, naming your truth, however difficult that may be. But avoiding advocating for yourself can be such a source of pain, both physical and mental. Also, changing the habits of a lifetime, untangling a lifetime of ignoring your own needs, takes commitment and courage and often needs the support of a friend or therapist or coach. The regular practice of self-compassion as meditation will also help shift neural pathways, so that speaking your truth becomes more the norm, and much less challenging than it was at the beginning.

I have a t-shirt that says, 'In a world where you can be anything, be kind.' I'm going to end this chapter on kindness. There can be a point in a day when you know it's kind of pivotal. It can literally go either way: the path of grumpiness - or alternatively, a path defined by a small act of kindness. I don't need to tell you which leaves us feeling better. Kindness is health-enhancing. The mental health charities know this. The Mental Health Foundation describes kindness as choosing to do something, that helps others or yourself, with genuine warm feelings. Note it remains important to act kindly to yourself, but it can be balanced healthily with an act of kindness that puts someone else's needs before your own. The obvious one is volunteering, giving up your time to serve someone else's needs can not only catalyse the physiological signals that contribute to wellbeing, but also can build connection and community. And as kindness begets kindness, others can see how they too might contribute.

My neighbours and friends are amongst the best in the world. As I have become more disabled, I've had to let go some of the things I used to enjoy. Setting out bedding plants in the spring always gave me great joy. My husband had taken over most other household chores, so he couldn't fit that in too. To my horror a large bush in the garden died. It was a home to many birds, and on occasion the local fox and family. And not only that, it had beautiful year-round leaves. Our friends volunteered and redesigned that part of the garden with our input. It's beautiful and they even placed a bird table in the centre, opposite the kitchen window. What a gift of their time, expertise, and vision. We were so delighted and grateful. A neighbour who also loved their garden kept it in good health. And not only that, they keeps my window boxes and other pots by the door full of fresh healthy flowers and plants. Kindness begets kindness. I've since then knitted items for a coming grandchild and so it continues. The pleasure the garden brings us has grown and grown. Even writing this gives me a glow because of all we have gained and the many shared conversations too.

Opportunities for random acts of kindness, such as sending a postcard, can pop up every day. Planned ones could include: adopt, don't shop, when getting a pet; buying second-hand; donating blankets to shelters, or food to foodbanks. As these acts mount up, we are truly creating a kinder society.

Self-compassion is a crucial part of wellbeing, and it is truly multifactorial. But it does need to be worked at and become an activity that is prioritised. Compassionate people and communities build compassionate nations. What more could we wish for to support wellbeing?

▮ Reflections for professionals

For any carers, formal or informal, the practice of self-compassion is crucial to wellbeing. Steve Covey's book on the *7 Habits of Highly Effective People* is often quoted and worth a read, especially when starting out in work and life! It's habit number 7, I want to highlight, 'Sharpening the Saw'. I want to tell you the parable of the Two Woodcutters in a local context!

One Day there were two woodcutters, let's say they were from Argyll. They were always arguing about who was best at chopping wood. Inevitably one day they decided to have a competition to see who could cut the most wood. The winner would stand the other one a pint at the George in Inveraray.

So next day they set up the task in the forest overlooking Loch Fyne. They both set out at pace and after an hour Finn noticed that he couldn't hear any chopping of wood from Iain. He has run out of steam already, he thought, and carried on confident of his superiority. After 15 minutes, Finn heard Iain. They both continued. Another hour passed and Finn chopped on, then realised that once more no noise of chopping was coming from Iain. This renewed Finn's optimism and he carried on. This continued all day, same thing each hour. When the finish came and time to assess the winner, Finn was confident. But that didn't last as it emerged that Iain had chopped down more trees than Finn. Finn asked, 'how can this be when you stopped every hour for a break?' Iain replied, "well, it's straightforward, every time I stopped work, while you carried on chopping down trees, I was sharpening my axe.'

What does this mean for you in a professional context? All that is written about self-care is relevant to all of us. But it's not just about mindfulness, practising gratitude, taking a break: it's also about pausing to learn about latest techniques, treatments and research, including the evidence by experience. Healthcare has been typically slow to adopt new practice. The pandemic has shown what is possible, when there is a shared objective and a passion for improvement. Practice-based evidence has been accepted as a valuable approach to progress, especially for conditions like long covid. Perhaps in the past taking time to learn about research may have seemed a luxury. The pandemic has shown it is sometimes the difference between life and death.

I know I've been guilty of being less than compassionate to myself. I have been that person who kept working at the expense of my health. I don't recommend that way to learn the messages of self-compassion. Many good people are lost to caring professions because they become exhausted and unwell, they fall out of love with what they do and feel unvalued. They've rarely sharpened the saw, and all their skills are lost. Too many people feel caught in a culture in the caring sector (both in public and maybe even more so in third sector settings) of needing to show how busy they are. How different would a mindful, skilled workforce look, prioritising instead living with and working with compassion. How different the experience of care would be. Of course, it needs to be properly resourced to achieve that.

A workforce that is poorly resourced and doesn't experience kindness or care for its own well-being will naturally find it hard to do that for others. Individuals will become depleted and drained of their resilience or desire to keep going. Working with people who need our care and compassion is one of the greatest gifts of our professional lives. As Viktor Frankyl has helped us see, finding our purpose and being able to live well is what feeds our wellbeing and our very soul. But we can't take that for granted in any workforce.

Caring for the carers is never more important than in recent times. Many were talking of leaving since the early years of the pandemic as the physical and emotional toll were overwhelming. At the same time universities are seeing huge increases in applications for qualifications in the caring professions. At one level care is being recognised as vitally important - but the lived experience of the work remains at odds with the rhetoric. Kindness must be built into the system and experienced both by those who work in it, and those who use the service. We also need it in political systems, communities, and nations, and like everything it starts with us as individuals.

Part Three

Reflections from my journey

A new long-term condition arrived.

I struggled with the name of this chapter. It's not *Conclusion*, because for me, and I expect for you, the learning continues. I certainly don't want this book to seem like I have all the answers: I don't. I hope in part I have posed questions to help you ask yourself at this stage in your life, whatever that is. I hope as well that the learning you have gathered from this work will help galvanise you to support yourself and help you know how best gain support from others.

While putting these words onto the page (they've been cooking a while in my head!), I have been very aware of the ongoing development of the long-term condition that's devastating lives across the world. The Office for National Statistics (ONS)[37] in July 2020 reported that 1.46% of people in the UK are living with long COVID-19, as it's been known. In January 2023 'An estimated 2.1 million people living in private households in the UK (3.3% of the population) were experiencing self-reported long COVID (symptoms continuing for more than four weeks after the first confirmed or suspected coronavirus (COVID-19) infection that were not explained by something else).[38]

This makes it a major long-term condition without a bespoke service, without real understanding of how it happens, of why only some people get it and of whether it will improve. The impact on individuals, on communities, on the workforce and the economy isn't yet known. Researchers into the 1918 Flu Pandemic showed similar post-viral lethargy (the most frequently described symptom in long covid). This was thought to have caused a severe famine in what is now Tanzania because the lethargy caused the population to be unable to attend to the crops. Pandemics affect so much is unforeseeable - we need to invest in research, so we understand how best to treat and support people affected.

The NHS, especially frontline staff like doctors, nurses, and carers, have been particularly affected. The ONS also assessed that at least 122,000 NHS staff in England have long covid and this not only has life-changing impact on them but also significantly affects staffing levels. A group of

---

[37] Office of National Statistics-Coronavirus (COVID-19) Infection Survey-Long Covid.

[38] Prevalence of ongoing symptoms following coronavirus (COVID-19) infection in the UK - Office for National Statistics (ons.gov.uk)

doctors belonging to a Facebook group were involved in a study and given the opportunity to work in facilitated groups to provide time with peers living with long covid.[39] In an extremely powerful section on moving forward, they described the insights gained by those taking part. I'm sharing them here in summary, as the findings are so relevant to all the work and ideas we have processed throughout this book.

- They needed to find new approaches to healing.

- They were disappointed medicine did not offer the answers.

- They realised the need for self-care and not to pressurise themselves.

- They were processing the loss of their previous selves.

- They accepted that the group enabled and helped them become more self-compassionate.

- They better understood what caring means; and the values of kindness, compassion (for self and others), and feeling heard.

- They felt changed as people and doctors.

- They pledged to listen and be more open to symptoms that don't fit with current understanding.

- They developed a much greater understanding of being disabled and living with a long-term condition.

The other parallels that long covid recognises are with CFS (chronic fatigue syndrome) and ME (myalgic encephalitis). The history of ME with the medical professions is not a happy one. And not just the medical profession – it was the media that coined the term 'yuppie flu', like it was a new accessory to a charmed life. The reality could not be further from that. These conditions developed after a virus and resulted in lost years of education, lost jobs, lost relationships. What made that worse was not being believed. At its worst it was thought of as child

[39] Learning from doctors with long covid - The BMJ

neglect, laziness, hysteria, or mental illness – those with symptoms generally being put in the 'difficult' category. I interviewed some people with ME, CFS and fibromyalgia and I heard such devastating stories from people who were so unwell and so misunderstood. By then the conditions had been recognised as neurological in their origins, and yet still health professionals were prone to judgement and were ill-informed about what might help. The WEL course I mentioned in my introduction was developed as a group process to meet the needs of many people struggling to live with these conditions. Just being truly heard was transformational. Self-management approaches have since been developed that enable people affected to take control over their situation. These use several techniques to support them to become more active and more engaged in time, while accepting they have a condition that can relapse.

The community who live with MS, CFS and Fibromyalgia have watched the development of long covid with interest. Many have spoken of their learning of how to live with a similar condition - and how to help people navigate a system that doesn't adapt flexibly to new, unseen conditions that are difficult to diagnose. Indeed, the current focus on long covid may help the wider community who live with similar conditions.

I hope the information and guidance in this book will help those living with long covid, although I designed the elements before the condition developed. Whether some medical interventions are in time found to help or not, nonetheless the approaches in the book will be valuable. My hope is that this is a publication that will be shared with people who are newly or recently diagnosed with long covid or any other long-term condition as well as living with cancer.

Recognising my own challenges.

Writing this also helped me identify how I have felt at difficult times, and what has helped me get through. I also recognised that writing some parts was harder than others. Two areas I found myself wanting to skip over were when I made the decision to leave being a charity leader, and about becoming disabled. Two major milestones in my life where this writing has taught me I still need to do some processing.

My own way of dealing with the hard stuff is to lift the lid a little bit and see how it is and if I'm ready to face it, then allow myself to look properly, write it down, talk it through – and, more recently, to find a way of sitting alongside it with loving kindness. All of them help, and then sometimes I need put the lid back on, or howl and cry, or all three. I suppose what I have learned from all of that is that you can't force this process; you can merely create the right conditions for it and trust yourself to know when the time is right. No 'you should be over this by now' or 'you should have a good cry'. But my biggest observation is you can't shut the lid on it forever.

My father's generation largely went off to war as young men. Men like my dad, who had grown up in rather untouched and sheltered parts of the UK and the world. They weren't a generation who had travelled, until the war took them across the globe. My Dad went from a village in Fife to Italy, Africa and almost to Burma but after the bomb was dropped on Hiroshima and the Japanese surrendered, their Royal Navy boat turned around and he came home. He met my Mum on his travels in England and they settled in Fife after a few years, had children, made friends, made careers and had a full life. He would occasionally share stories from those times when his world was a dangerous place, and you would get a small glance at the stories that had in turn shaped him. I remember how he once told us about a boat torpedoed near him: men fell into the sea only to be eaten by tiger sharks. A scene even David Attenborough would want to spare you from. Another time, towards the end of the war, his ship led the flotilla into the bay of Naples expecting to meet the Italian and German Fleets. He spoke of how they didn't expect to come through the battle, but how history had another plan. It was that moment when the Italians decided to surrender. Not only was there monumental relief, but there was also a party that lasted several days. He retained a love of Italian Opera from that time. I know it affected his politics and he was incredibly careful about saying much at all - until he was dying. Unlike many men who found retirement gave them the space to think about it all, my father kept busy.

Health and social care found they were dealing with many men of his generation who experienced depression and low mood in the 1980's and 1990's, retiring from work and then finding themselves retraumatised by the memories from war that they had tucked away. For my dad it was the last months of his life when he revisited some of it. One of the triggers was an album we bought him by Kiri te Kanawa. It had a simply exquisite version of *'O' mio babbino caro'*. 'Oh, my dear father' not only reminded him of Italy: it was also a reminder of his own father who had died young. Our tears flowed with him - my dad who never cried - as he recalled the loss of his father and the loss of friends, the loss of childhood, and the loss of a simpler, kinder world too. He also touched on deeper painful memories - but mostly he took those ones to his grave. His tears and memories were so painful that I still cry freely when I hear that aria. Men and women from this era relived the horrific impact of war once their lives allowed them the space. Conversely, the generations since then have been fed a Dad's Army version of war time, with the signature tune by Vera Lynn. How hard it must have been to try to process a much darker reality. Without recourse to yoga and meditation, they were stuck with the stiff upper lip - or alcohol - and some were prescribed diazepam.

There was research done looking at people who survived the concentration camps. They rarely returned home because their homes were devastated. Many needed to get away from Europe and went on to new lives on different continents. Psychiatrists researched how those who survived were able to get on with their lives. They rarely sought help for the trauma they had survived - the interesting finding was that it was the next generation who needed the help. The trauma had been held and passed on. As the study of epigenetics[40] shows, trauma doesn't disappear.

The best thing we can do to help the next generation is to show them why denial doesn't work long-term. We need to help people learn to process trauma, how to tell their truths, how to be self-compassionate and share loving kindness. My dad was generally open to new things, but the talking therapies were a different country for him. We have their generation to thank for ours doing the exploration to find the concept of good health is wider than eating fresh vegetables, taking cod-liver oil, and drinking orange juice!

[40] https://youtu.be/yEh3JG74C6s

The Ten Elements Revisited.

The ten elements came to me as I thought of this work. They are mainly about how we ourselves live with serious illness and long-term conditions, and not the conditions themselves. It is my hope that people will become more able to manage their lives with peace and optimism. I hope, too, that as you work through the book, you will gain confidence to be your own advocates. Our experience of treatment and support may not be as person-centred and compassionate as we would want and our right to shared decision-making may not be recognised. Advocacy becomes a central skill to help us negotiate the care we need.

I mentioned how some people with long covid and, for decades, ME and fibromyalgia, have not necessarily been believed when they sought care and treatment. This isn't peculiar to those conditions either. Chronic pain for example, without any diagnosed organic problem, can also be in that category. We can't see pain: we can only see its impact. And many who don't understand tend to think, well *you take pain relief so that's the end of it*. But painkillers rarely deal with pain completely, and I know from my own experience that a balance needs to be struck between side effects and functioning in the world. Recently I spoke to a family member who had severe pain after an injury. Thankfully this was improving but she had become more sensitised to my situation, how losing my mobility had been difficult, but the nerve pain was worse. In many ways it's the pain that is the limiter of my world. I've learned to be in a better relationship to it, and that's helped me retain my mental and physical health.[41] Self-management programmes do help enormously and can give you the confidence to stretch your physical boundaries too. All the insights covered in the ten elements will help. Even if you have lived a long time with a condition and associated pain, support to self-manage can make a significant difference.

Mental health is a theme I haven't covered in detail, but low mood is likely to accompany any serious illness and long-term condition. There is no predicting when this will happen; we are all different and all have varied resilience what triggers anxiety and depression. Effects on mental health also show up in different ways. For me, I recognise it's usually less about feeling low - what happens is I just slow up: everything becomes

[41] Chronic pain: an update on burden, best practices, and new advances - The Lancet

difficult, a mountainous terrain to navigate. Often, I don't realise this initially, and so I can be slow to seek help. It is recognised in medicine that many conditions will trigger depression, but this is rarely screened for. Maybe we can accept a level of low mood as part of a normal adjustment to a major change in life and health. Again, self-compassion techniques are likely to help, and peer support can also help to lift mood and grow optimism. It is important not to lose quality of life, so anyone feeling concerned about their mood should seek help. All the things I explore here are all meant to sit alongside traditional treatments and aren't an alternative. Dr David Reilly, who developed The WEL and more recently the COVIDWEL (developed for those living with the impact of COVID-19), describes three sides of a triangle: one prevention, one treatment and the other the resilience of the host. All the 10 elements help towards our physical and mental resilience.

I wrote this book over a period like no other in recent times. Now approaching the end of this journey, I take another look at all the elements and invite you to do this alongside me.

■ Looking back-looking forward

Element One: Know who you are.

> As I went through all the exercises, I naturally reviewed my own self-awareness. Living through the pandemic and lockdowns, I have learned more about myself. I realise I need less things or travels or friends even than I thought - the only thing I want is more time for the people who matter. I have found being less busy very valuable. Not just to give me time with family, but also time to reflect. The challenge now, as the pandemic is less impactful, is how do I continue to protect that time?

Element Two: Understand your values.

> Writing this has reminded me that my valuing of kindness and compassion has deepened. In many ways, too, I notice it is both simple, and yet paradoxically really challenging.

Element Three: What are your strengths?

I have found I can stay calm and find a way through, whatever the challenge. That's not been tested as much since becoming disabled and I'm glad to be reminded of that. It's something others appreciate in me, I've been told. The calmness under fire has helped me through so much.

Element Four: Who brings you joy?

Haven't we all had that put into sharp focus of late? I have learned the importance of being around the right people over many years. I am fortunate to have several meaningful friendships and a wonderful family who have sustained me through the many challenges of late. I'm so grateful for my family, and my deep friendships which bring me warmth and love and joy.

Element Five: Work with your health and social care team as partners in your care.

This has been increasingly difficult as all the processes of care have changed so much through and since the pandemic. In the main my healthcare has been fine over this time, and I've had vaccines and boosters. But I've lost continuity of care initially from my GP, which was a significant loss for me, especially given the complexity of my situation. But I bless the physiotherapists in the hydrotherapy unit, as they have almost literally held me get through the pain and loss of becoming disabled.

I initially found social care a significant disappointment. When I seek advice from occupational therapists to prevent me falling, it ended up in discussions about what the council will pay for. Perhaps the pandemic caused increasing pressure, taking time away from occupational therapists' and social workers' work in the areas of advice and prevention. Reducing skilled practitioners to jailors of the budget can't help anyone, least of all of them. But more recently an OT (occupational therapist) has enabled me to access care and respite through direct payments. This has been life changing. I waited a painful four months for the OT but she was excellent, both practical and compassionate. She also anticipated my needs and helped me work through resistance skilfully.

What I believe is very important, now, and always is that health and social care practitioners aren't removed from the human dynamic of their role. Care is an art as well as a science and healing so much more than treatment.

Element Six: Learn from lived experience.

The routes to this have so often been blocked recently. The means of engagement with those with similar lived experience shifted online, and for me and many others that's not been enough. There is a dilemma: if moving around takes huge energy and causes pain, then being able to remain in your own home is appealing. But this is at the expense of human contact and off-line conversations that engage in person and mean so much. My greatest support over the years of poor health has been the Maggie's Centre. Charities like this have considerable impact on families and individuals.[42]

Element Seven: Learn how to process what has happened.

Now 'what has happened' includes the pandemic and its accompanying fear, anxiety, sleeplessness and so on - even if we felt removed from the worst of it. The first stage of the pandemic made me very fearful for those I love and beyond that, our community and country. Acceptance of our fragility as a species was part of this. And for me as a disabled woman with a genetic disorder that makes me at higher risk of cancer, I was reminded daily of my own frailty. I had my last surgery a mere month before lockdown. Lockdown was almost like being preserved in time. We hit the pause button and I'm still adjusting and accommodating to the changes this produced in my body and my life. But it has taught me that I'm stronger than I look - I like that.

Element Eight: Understand more about grief and loss.

I lost four friends during lockdown. We managed to attend one socially distant funeral and it was grim. When we hug others, we are both transmitter and receiver of love, yet we were stuck with our arms wrapped around ourselves, shedding lonely tears. This is not

---

[42] Macmillan Cancer Support | The UK's leading cancer care charity

how to grieve. No wake, no storytelling ritual - of both the sad and happy tales: so much loss remains from this awful time. The longer-term impact on mental health is already being seen. I know I have many more tears to shed.

Many of us have qualified our own losses, saying they are nothing compared to those of many others. But grief isn't rationed, is relative, and shouldn't be compared. You feel what you feel. And what you feel is valid.

Element Nine: Nature and nurture.

As we stocked up at the beginning of lockdown, access to healthy food became an obsession. I never succumbed to toilet roll hoarding, but if you need a tin of chickpeas do call. I shouted Vitamin D3 to anyone who would listen. I had already lobbied family for some time, and I think they finally listened. I learned too that Omega 3 plays an important part of shoring up the immune response, so I'm supplementing that too. Nurture is about so much more than food, but food is a central need.

And finally...

Element Ten: Self-compassion.

Making kindness, compassion, self-care, and gratitude a part of my daily life has been the biggest shift for me in recent years. I'm not perfect at it. I can still judge myself against my own high standards, but I can embrace settling for good enough more often. Perhaps age is a factor, but alongside gaining wrinkles I recognise have been on a spiritual path . . . and that's a longer but compelling journey.

As the pandemic's global impact remains, I make no apology for this book really being an invitation to know and care for yourself. Of course, that involves compassion for others - but we can't change other people. We can only change ourselves. It's not selfish, it's just self-care and we are the only ones who can do that.

Leadership and Culture.

So many people I know have said how much they have enjoyed not running around so much during the lockdown. Sugar is maybe the worst addiction we need to tackle, but our the busy-all-the-time addiction (BALT) also needs attention.

I went cold turkey when I left a senior position when its constant busyness finally broke me, given I was recovering from major illness too. Eventually, as my fatigue eased, the loop of recurrent chest infections I was on stopped. As I was less exhausted, and I had time to grieve my health and that part of my career, I found a new energy for a different career, one that I could manage. I was fortunate I had choices; many don't. My belief is that leaders need to create a different workplace culture, and free the workforce to work in a way that fosters energy and creativity.

My experience has taught me that if you give people a vision and the means to deliver it, they will do their absolute best to do so. We don't need targets and judgements. We naturally give of our best if we feel valued and part of a community. Four-day weeks are worth pursuing, but not if the culture of presenteeism doesn't change and the zero hours contracts continue to devalue and damage a workforce. We work exceptionally long hours in the UK, and we have poor productivity compared to most of Europe. If we can create a future where all workers are valued, family time is valued and more democratic workplaces value physical and mental wellbeing, productivity will improve.

The pandemic has been devastating for so many businesses and their staff and clients. Furloughing enabled them to keep going, uncertainty. But for some the pandemic helped people unleash their innate creativity, and we've seen businesses go on-line, shift to producing PPE (personal protective equipment), focus on the local rather than global and much more. A crisis produces the fight/flight mechanisms in the body that can energise and cut through resistance to produce solutions that in other times may have been rejected, using all the familiar excuses. In the public sector, bureaucracy became more flexible during the pandemic, enabling change to be implemented more quickly, and staff responded eagerly. That hasn't been sustained in many places